The Sound of Turquoise

The Sound of Turquoise

Gill Gregory

KU
PRESS

KINGSTON UNIVERSITY
PRESS

Kingston University Press Ltd, Kingston University,
Penrhyn Road, Kingston upon Thames
Surrey KT1 2EE

Contents © Gill Gregory 2009

The right of the above author to be identified as the author of
this work has been asserted in accordance with the
Copyright, Designs and Patent Act 1988.

British Library Cataloguing in Publication Data available.

ISBN 978-1-899999-46-0

Set in Palatino
Typeset by: Legend Press Ltd, London
www.legendpress.co.uk

Printed in the UK by Beamreach Printing

Cover concept and image: July3rd Designs
Cover design production: Robert Mann
Cover photo courtesy of Dinah Gregory

KINGSTON UNIVERSITY
PRESS

For my family

Contents

Acknowledgements

I would like to thank Siobhan Campbell, Meg Jensen and Alison Hill at Kingston University Press for their invaluable editorial support, insight and helpful criticism.

I would also like to thank the following friends, colleagues and research bodies for their encouragement and ideas in the writing of this book: Betty and Laurie Bradbury, Tricia Bickerton, Robert Chandler, Nicholas Clark at the Britten-Pears Library, Simone Coxall, Elizabeth and Mary Cuthbert, Wendy French, Margaret Garlake, Roberta Gilbert, Nicholas, Marion and Annabel Gregory, Leslie Hall at the Wellcome Institute, Marigold Hoare, Wojciech Janik at the UCL School of Slavonic & East European Studies, Pam Jarvis, Sally Kilmister, Laura Marcus, Monica McCaffrey at SIBS, Neil Macintyre, Calum MacLeod, Adrian McLachlan, Michael Morpurgo, Michael Murphy, Ida Newton, Leonee Ormond, Harriet Parks, Edith Gilchrist and Victoria Rea at the Royal Free Archive, Deryn Rees-Jones, Andrew Roberts, Peter Basham at The Royal College of Physicians, David Stevens, the staff at Tate Britain, Andrew Teverson, Mark Turner, the students and staff at The University of Notre Dame, Bernard and Nadia Valman, Lynne Walker and Jane Leighton at the Institute of Historical Research, Anna Wojnowicz and Izabella at the Pavement Café, the staff at Clapham Books and Waterstones, and my neighbours, Lucy Furlonge and Dimple Ghumman.

Especial thanks to my mother for all her love, inspiration and generosity over the years and to Robert, Liz and Lucy Gregory for their companionship, ideas and unwavering belief in my work. This book is dedicated to them.

Preface

In my life I have attempted to leave behind the girl in my memory. She was a child who grew up with an elder brother suffering from a very severe form of epilepsy, and as he grew older, his seizures became more violent and disturbing. This girl loved her brother passionately and thought that her own suffering was minor, by contrast with his. To tell anyone about her difficulties would, she believed, be a betrayal of the first order.

In the process of writing about my brother a small girl began to emerge. I realised that this child was still a comparative stranger. She was a girl who had lived largely in her imagination. She made all the right noises at school, at home and in public, and yet her inner life (which felt to her more real) was one that was hidden for the most part. She had tucked this private world away so effectively, she barely knew it herself.

The girl in this book has emerged to the point at which she can almost look her readers in the eye, even though she is reluctant to do so. I have attempted to tell the story of her active but very dislocated imagination. This girl has needed to set things straight and, in the process of her story being told, her life has begun to assume greater coherence.

The girl is flanked by her grandfather and her brother. They represent the two poles of her imagination, between which she moves in space and time. She looks to them both and in their stories she finds something of herself.

1

Sea Piece

1961

A small girl in a scarlet tutu and pink silk ballet shoes led seven girls onto a large stage. She had little idea of why or where she was leading them, but enjoyed the sensation of pointing her toes and stretching and curving her arms. Each girl's tutu was a different colour – scarlet, emerald green, indigo, silver, gold, pink, white and yellow. In their silk bodices and skirts of layered netting, the seven, eight and nine year old girls were supposed to resemble an assortment of twinkling fish living in the depths of the ocean. The girls had been drafted in from ballet schools in Surrey and London to dance in a fifteen-minute work, *Sea Piece*, which was being performed at a theatre near Bloomsbury.

Meg, the nine year old girl in the scarlet tutu, was already out of breath when the lights dimmed and the maroon velvet curtain went up to gasps of pleasure from the audience. The stage was swathed in shimmering blue satins and silks, scattered with shells of every shape, size and colour. In the middle there were some large grey cardboard rocks coated with a slimy green substance to resemble seaweed. A mermaid with a turquoise tail was curled up in a sandy grotto to the left of the rocks, and in front of her a golden sea creature, half fish and half man, was hopping from side to side.

A single grand piano in the pit was playing a haunting sea legend by a composer born in Paris at the turn of the century.

Meg and her friend, Susie, who wore a silver tutu, had lost themselves backstage on their way to the make-up room. The two girls had wandered up and down corridor after corridor until they ran into one of the stage hands, who returned them to make-up. There they were quickly powdered and rouged and an out-of-breath Meg had little time to think of what kind of entrance she was making, when her moment came.

Although she liked her tutu and pumps and could manage the steps with a degree of finesse, she didn't like ballet as it involved too many exercises and she had to keep in step with the other girls. Meg had been very surprised that the ballet teacher at the theatre had chosen her to lead the little fish girls on stage. She liked being the first in the line, though.

As Meg danced forward she was caught up in the undulating waves of the silky landscape. The blues, silvers and golds were breathtaking and the applause tumultuous as the girls made their entrance. They then joined hands in a circle and skipped around before scattering to the edges of the stage, where they sat or lay depending on what kind of fish they were.

Meg was a sea-horse and wore a little gold cardboard coronet on her head. She held herself still and straight as if she were swimming upright. She had to sit without fidgeting as that was what sea-horses did. The delicate creatures liked to bob gently in sea grass meadows, their brown and grey rings of colour merging with the fields. If a sea-horse was surprised by another fish, she could turn bright yellow or orange or red.

Sea Piece was about a man whose top half was transformed by a mermaid into a sea creature, with his other half from the waist down remaining a man. All the dancers were girls except for the woman and man who played the

14

mermaid and the creature. *Sea Piece* came in between two longer ballets, *Sunken City I and II*, performed by adult dancers.

From the side of the stage Meg watched the mermaid and the fish man for a while, admiring their shiny costumes and the way they spun around and pirouetted, even the mermaid who had pink scaly shoes peeping out from beneath her turquoise tail. The creature-man was dressed in green pumps and a golden leotard and over his face he wore a scaly silver mask. Every so often he leapt over to the sides of the stage on the tips of his green toes and, in a swirl of gold, he gazed into the eyes of the little fish girls. Meg could see the dancer's pretty blue eyes through the eye-holes when he danced close by.

Meg looked into the auditorium to see if she could spot her mother and father, but when she peered into the darkness and at the shapes it held, she could not distinguish them. Vasili and Jane had arrived fifteen minutes or so before *Sea Piece* was due to begin, so had missed *Sunken City I*.

Vasili had grown up in a garden square close by, and after the ballet he and Meg were to visit his father, Alexis, while Jane drove back to their Surrey village. Meg's older brother, Andrew, suffered from epilepsy and they had left him for the afternoon in the care of a nurse.

Meg gave up trying to find her parents in the audience and turned to watch the mermaid and the sea-creature, her body pleasurably caught up in the gentle rhythms and melodies played on the piano in the pit. She began to think about the grandfather she was to meet for the first time in her life.

Alexis already had a strong hold on Meg's imagination. Her mother admired her father-in-law, her blue eyes lighting up whenever Meg asked about him. Meg knew that her grandfather had run away to England from Russia because he wanted to see the world, and that he was a doctor who could 'work miracles'. Her mother said that his patients called him 'the little Russian faith healer', because people with very stiff legs and bodies could stand up and walk again after his treatments.

A few months ago Jane and Vasili had told her the whole truth of Alexis's history. His entire family had been lined up by bandits in a field on their farm in Tashkent – his mother and father, brothers and sisters, and Alexis. The family had all been shot dead, except for her grandfather who the bandits missed, because he was short for his age.

'When it was safe and the bandits had gone, your grand-father, who was only fourteen years old, made his way to England and trained as a doctor. He was very, very brave. He is only five feet, Meg – not much taller than you. One day when he was younger, just a baby, he sat on the Tsar of Russia's lap.'

Meg looked up at her mother in amazement. She was both shocked and mesmerised by the story. Her grandfather had been very lucky to stay alive. She asked her mother why they never saw Alexis. 'Because, Meg, he and Daddy had a big disagreement and they have not spoken to each other for a very long time.'

Meg liked the sound of his name and chanted it under her breath – Alexis, Alexis, Alexis – from where she was sitting at the side of the stage. Her sea-horse head was nodding but she woke in time, as the little sea creatures suddenly leapt up onto their feet.

Sea Piece finished with the creature and the mermaid emerging from the depths of the ocean, their heads break-ing through the silk and satin waves into the spotlight. Accompanied by the quickening tempo of the piano and in a shower of silver dust cascading from above, the top half of the creature turned back into a human being and the mermaid changed into a woman, her turquoise tail flopping about on the stage. The little fish girls danced in a ring around them.

Everyone in the audience was clapping hard. The pianist stood up and the mermaid-turned-woman waved him onto the stage to take a bow with the cast, who were smiling and gesturing to the audience. They took three curtain calls and accepted bouquets of bright flowers brought onto the stage by the director from the wings, who also took a bow. As the applause died down, some of the audience got up to stretch their legs or went to the bar for a drink before *Sea Piece II* began. A few, including Vasili and Jane, got up to leave.

They collected Meg from the big dressing room backstage, where the girls quickly changed out of their fish costumes back into their own clothes. Meg's eyes were green with a black speck in her left eye, which people found pretty. She had inherited her Russian grandfather's smallness and was short for her age. Her frame looked strong but slight and this created a curious sense of the girl's figure being something you could not quite pin down.

The family's pale blue Ford Zephyr was parked in a side street near the theatre. Vasili had bought the two-door convertible in the spring and at weekends the family drove all over Surrey, with the roof down if the weather was fine. They visited Boxhill and Epsom Downs, but Meg and her brother's favourite trip was to Leith Hill. With the car parked in a lane, the siblings would run on ahead of their parents and scramble up the steep hill to the turreted tower on the summit. Then they would leap up the narrow staircase inside the tower, Andrew first with Meg close behind him, to emerge at the top, where they shouted and waved to their parents down below.

Vasili and Meg kissed Jane goodbye before she drove home. It was half past four and Alexis was expecting Meg and her father at five. Vasili took Meg's hand and they started to walk slowly in the direction of Bloomsbury. Meg was bursting to meet Alexis. Her father's slow movements often irritated her. She compared him with her grandfather, who had run so quickly away from Russia he was completely out of breath.

They walked up Goodge Street past jewellers and grocers, fruit and vegetable stalls, and a girl by the underground station selling violet posies for your buttonhole. Alexis's flat was in one of the big garden squares on the other side of the main road. As they were early, Vasili decided to take Meg on a short tour of the area he knew so well. He cut through a series of small squares and then stopped by a red-brick building on a corner. They stood in front of a portico with cream columns and gazed up at a large four-storey house. Meg counted eight windows on each floor.

'Who lives there, Dad?' she asked.

'This is The London School of Medicine for Women,' said Vasili, turning to Meg with tears in his green eyes, 'where your grandmother, Hazel, trained to be a doctor over fifty years ago.'

Meg knew both her grandparents were doctors like her father, but had never heard of a school for women learning about medicines. She wondered why they didn't just go to the school the men went to. Or did the women take special medicine which was for them only? She didn't ask Vasili these questions as she thought he might burst into tears, and she didn't want him to, especially without her mother there. Her father cried easily.

'Your grandmother was a doctor who treated children. She was a very great woman.'

Vasili's mother had died nine years ago in January 1952. Remembering Hazel was making her father very sad, so Meg asked him where they were going next. Vasili looked vague and uneasy. He turned away from the training school and walked with Meg toward the big square where Alexis lived.

On the way he stopped in a smaller square, beside a gas lamp in front of another large building. There was an arched doorway and a portico and lots of tall rectangular windows.

'What is this building, Dad?'

Again tears filled his eyes. Vasili replied that it was The National Hospital. 'This is where Mum and I bring Andrew when a doctor needs to see him about his epilepsy. It's a hospital for people who have *petit mals*, Meg.'

Meg liked the building and the small square with trees and railings. She gazed at the tall gas lamp, which made her think of Lucy in *The Lion, The Witch & The Wardrobe*. In Narnia there was lots of bad magic. Andrew's epileptic fits were like bad magic. Her brother had some giant or witch inside him, punching and biting and kicking his head so that he had a fit, and then Andrew's body went rigid and started jerking, with his arms stuck out like he was going to hug you, only he wasn't – his arms got stuck and went back and forward, back and forward like a machine, until the fits ended, and then Andrew returned to whatever it was he was doing before. He returned to normal and she did too.

She wished someone could wave a wand and make the fits disappear for good. Maybe Andrew would be happier if he was turned to stone by the witch in Narnia, because then he wouldn't have any more fits. He was in agony all the time, especially when he bit right through his tongue really hard and spat blood. Then his tongue swelled up and became unbelievably sore. For a long time after that he could only sip lukewarm soup and porridge and melting ice-cream, with blood leaking out of his mouth.

'Why don't the doctors in the hospital make Andrew's fits go away, Dad?'

'It's not as simple as that, Meg. Andrew's brain was damaged when he was born, which means he will always have epilepsy. The doctors can give him medicine so that he doesn't have so many fits. There is nothing else they can do.'

Meg instinctively turned away from the red-brick bearing down on her. The building was a prison or like the hospital in Epsom where her father worked and mad people screamed and mumbled to themselves beneath the trees. Meg never wanted to go there. If Jane collected Vasili from the hospital in the early evening, Meg would sit in the car waiting, while her mother went into the grounds.

Vasili and Meg made their way west. Meg was wondering what would happen if her mother and father died and she had to look after Andrew. How *could* she? She would have to give him his medicine and make sure he didn't run away like he did every so often. What would happen if she wanted to go to university like the teachers at school and her parents said she should? What would happen then? These were terrible thoughts. She felt guilty that she didn't want to look after Andrew like her mother did all the time. She hated the epilepsy.

The big square was much larger than the others they had walked through and the garden in the middle, with its tall trees, seemed forlorn. There were huge blocks of flats and an enormous hotel Meg didn't like the look of. She was disappointed that her grandfather lived in this square. She liked the other ones much better.

Alexis lived on the south side of the square, on the second floor of one of the mansion blocks, where Vasili and his parents lived when he was a boy. Meg didn't care where he lived anymore. *Sea Piece* and the entrancing colours of the ballet drained away, and all she could recollect was the mermaid's turquoise tail flopping about on the stage. Stupid, she thought. That looked really stupid.

Inside, the hall was very quiet. There were wooden pigeonholes with letters for the residents tucked inside – a couple were stuffed full, whilst others were completely empty, cleaned out by whoever's name was below the box – Appleby, Bernard and so on. Meg spotted the name 'Chodak' and tugged the sleeve of her father's tweed jacket.

'Is that Alexis, Dad? Is it? Is it?'

She had never met anyone else called Chodak so surely this was her grandfather. He made up the name when he arrived in England, her mother said. Meg thought it sounded like the name of her mother's box camera.

Meg's right knee began shaking, like she couldn't possibly wait for whatever she was anticipating. Her knee shook as much as Andrew's body did in a fit, but she could stop the shaking. Her brother couldn't. Her father didn't notice her knee shaking.

'Yes, darling. That's your grandfather. We'll go up to his flat in the lift.'

It was nine years since he had seen his father at his mother's funeral. On that cold January day Jane had been three months pregnant with Meg, and Andrew's epilepsy was growing worse. Today he had come to see Alexis as his father had undergone a mild stroke at the age of seventy. He had written to his son asking him to visit and 'let bygones be bygones as the English say'.

Meg did not understand what a stroke was. It sounded like stroking the cat which was nice. Her mother had told her that Alexis's mind was muddled, so he might seem rather strange when she met him, but that she wasn't to worry. Lots of people had strokes.

The lift was small and stuffy and the machinery was old. When the lift began to move upwards, it felt like a strong man from a circus was hauling them up out of a pit. At last it clanked to a halt on the second floor and Meg and Vasili were relieved to get out. Alexis lived at Flat 14G. The number was on a silver plate beside the door and Vasili gave the buzzer one short, sharp ring. Meg could hear someone shuffling toward the door and then there he was.

Meg's mood changed and there she was, with Alexis's warm, stubby hand on her head, his other arm reaching up around his taller son's shoulders. She was so close to Alexis in height, whilst at five feet ten Vasili towered over them. Meg felt a kinship, an affinity with this little old man who had a fairground, circus air about him. He was very stocky – he might have been a gymnast or the smallest strong man in the world, held aloft at the top of a pyramid of acrobats, arms wide open to embrace his audience – or a grown-up child exploding from a cannon into the silk and velvet laps of the front row, where he was welcomed and kissed and set on his feet.

The ballet in the afternoon, her red tutu, the mermaid, the creature man, all the colours of the rainbow up there on the stage, they all came back to Meg in her grandfather's hall as he ushered her into his small sitting-room. The notes of the French music played on the piano in the orchestra pit, returned to her. She felt pretty and light and pleasurably caught up inside the laughter in Alexis's voice.

Her father's laugh sounded uncomfortable and forced beside Alexis. Sadness suited him better. Jane told Meg that when her father was a boy, Alexis and Hazel took him to watch some scenes from Shakespeare's *The Merchant of Venice*. The actors played the scene beneath a cedar tree in one of their friend's big gardens. Vasili had been struck by the merchant Antonio's words at the beginning of the play: *I know not why I am so sad....*

A loud voice was booming in Alexis's sitting-room. It was coming from the small black and white television that had been turned up full volume. Alexis turned to Meg and pointed at the screen. Cows were being milked and a man in front of them with a microphone was speaking in a foreign language Meg didn't understand. The man sounded like he was singing the words. Alexis was chuckling at the Welsh news. There were tears in his eyes.

'Look at the cows, my little one – see how funny they are. I cannot understand what on earth the man is saying but I know these cows!'

He patted Meg on her head again and she wished he would keep doing that. She was a cat purring. Vasili looked uneasy, guarded. He waited for his father to calm down.

A long crimson-covered sofa filled most of the small room. There was an old, unlit gas fire in the hearth emitting a faint smell of bad eggs. Some small rosewood tables were placed around the room and two standard lamps, with dark green shades, were glowing softly. This might be an ocean, Meg thought. We have sunk into the deep green sea like in the ballet.

The walls were magnolia and a very old Turkish carpet covered the floor. Meg felt comfortable in this room as she had on the stage. She might lie on the carpet and be transported to Tashkent where her grandfather used to live.

In one corner of the room, beside an oak lectern with a script on it, there was a large standing vase painted with a pattern of indigo damsons, the dark blue fruit against a green background. Meg felt like hugging the vase and its fruit.

Alexis went over to the lectern and stood there turning over the pages, humming under his breath. Meg knew from her mother that her grandfather had a baritone voice. She wasn't sure exactly what 'baritone' was but the word sounded soft and round. Meg could see the musical notes on the page Alexis was studying and hoped he might start singing, but he moved away from the lectern and shook Vasili's hand again, before pulling a bell rope on the wall. You could hear it ringing somewhere near the hall and in under a minute a middle-aged woman, in a check pinafore, came into the room.

'This is Molly,' Alexis announced as if she were someone famous. 'She cooks and looks after me. Molly, is the tea ready? I think the little one and my son here are very hungry. Meg has been dancing.'

Alexis winked at Meg who blushed and smiled. He took both her hands in his and did a little jig and a whirl around with her, chuckling all the time. Vasili was annoyed and turned toward Molly. 'Yes, tea please. That would be marvellous.' He nodded at her as if tea were a rather dreadful meal in the circumstances. Meg thought her father looked like a policeman about to arrest you, like the 'bobby' in *Dixon of Dock Green* who said 'Evening all' at the beginning of the TV programme. Meg loved the sound of the policeman's voice and imagined her father wearing a hard black helmet. Evening all.

Alexis ushered Vasili and Meg into the kitchen, which led off the sitting-room, and left the door open. A large card table was set out for tea. Meg wondered why there was no tablecloth. The table was like the one at which she and her family played games. They didn't eat at such a table.

'Do you want me to keep the television on, sir, as usual?' Molly asked.

Alexis found the background noise reassuring. As a doctor he knew all about strokes. He was seventy and well aware that he would have to be very, very careful if he was to avoid a major stroke felling him before he grew old. That he was already old never crossed his mind. There were so many adventures to come.

'Yes, Molly – you know I want the television on.'

Alexis gazed at Vasili. What would her father say? Meg wondered. Will he be cross? At home tea was in the sitting-room. There was the breakfast room for breakfast and lunch and the room was also used for playing games, watching television and for parties. Recently her father had begun seeing his mad patients on the couch in the breakfast room and this meant she and Andrew missed programmes like *Bootsie & Snudge*, which was very funny. Bootsie and Snudge were servants who worked in 'a gentlemen's club'. No families were allowed into the club. It was very unfair of her father to use the breakfast room for his patients.

Vasili said nothing about the television being on. You could hear a man talking about DIY, how to put up shelves in three easy steps. Alexis laughed, 'I can put up the shelves. One! Two! Three! I am good at that, my boy!' Meg's father did not make things for the house, but that was because he was very busy thinking about his patients and his dreams.

She was very hungry and enjoyed the cheese and tomato sandwiches, followed by chocolate cake with lots of icing. There was a huge blue pottery bowl with fruit – apples and bananas, oranges and clusters of black grapes, stacked high, for afterwards. She drank lemonade while Vasili and Alexis had strong china tea, with thin slices of lemon and no milk.

Alexis said the tea made him think of Tashkent. 'I drank this tea when I was a boy.' He winked at Meg, 'You took it without the milk and with plenty of gravel sugar!' Meg thought 'gravel' was laid on roads. She was amazed when her grandfather stirred four heaped teaspoons of brown sugar into his tea. She had two teaspoons and her father, one.

'There is not a dining-room here,' Alexis smiled. 'I like to eat in the kitchen!'

Meg noticed her grandfather was dribbling out of both sides of his mouth. He was fumbling with the large white napkin, after pulling it out of the silver ring, so her father stood up to help him tuck it into the top of his shirt. Alexis was dressed in a green velvet smoking jacket and bow-tie, so it was difficult finding any room for the napkin. Eventually Vasili gently undid the tie, opened the top button of his shirt and tucked in the crumpled cloth. Alexis laughed and threw the tie on the floor.

The rest of the meal was quiet as Alexis was intent on his food. Every so often he glanced each side of him at Vasili and Meg. There they were. After the sandwiches and cake, Meg ate a banana and an orange Vasili peeled for her. Had her father forgiven Alexis or was it the other way round? Alexis's eyes were dark brown and they twinkled.

As Meg looked up from eating the segments of orange, her grandfather gazed into her eyes. 'Ah, they are green' he murmured, 'and something else.'

'My dear, you are a little elf child. Do you know about the tiny black speck, the dot in your left eye? Only the elf children have the dot and it means you are special. Your eyes dance, my dear. Is not that true, my son?'

Meg could see her father was very cross. Why did he hate Alexis? Her grandfather was more like a child than a grown-up.

'Your father is in a temper with me, I think, Meg? His eyes, they are filled up with a storm!'

Meg looked down at her plate and Alexis changed the subject.

'How is your boy, Vasili? Maybe I can help him? I know his brain is damaged but they say I heal with my hands. No, don't look at me like that, Vasili. You do not believe, I know. But I place my hands on his poor head and see if I can help. Maybe I can, maybe I cannot, but you could let me try? I am a doctor, Vasili!'

Her father threw down his napkin.

'Father, you know nothing about Andrew's condition! Thinking you can perform miracles when the truth is, Father, my son's epilepsy will only get worse. To give him false hope would be unforgivable. I respect your medical knowledge, Father, but I have no time for this nonsense of 'healing hands'. Why you chose to train in *medical gymnastics* of all things is beyond me!'

Meg was fascinated and frightened. What were 'medical gymnastics'? Why were 'healing hands' nonsense? Alexis and Vasili were still in the argument and everything was bleak once more. Soon she and her father would leave to catch the train. She noticed that familiar expression of contempt on her father's face, which made her feel cold all over.

They stayed another half hour, sitting round the unlit fire. Alexis was dozing, so Vasili turned the television off and drank his coffee in silence. Meg played with her grandfather's solitaire. She placed the large round board on one of the rosewood tables and tried over and over to end up with a single blue marble ball in the centre.

Vasili woke Alexis gently when they got up to leave. In the hall Alexis kissed them both. 'Goodbye, Meg. Until we meet again. When you come next I tell you a very long story.' He looked cautiously at Vasili.

As Vasili and Meg were about to turn away, Alexis suddenly placed his hand on his son's shoulder. 'Wait, my son. Wait! I have something.' He disappeared into his bedroom across the hall and Vasili and Meg could hear him rummaging through drawers. After a minute or so Alexis reappeared holding a large brown envelope, which he handed to Vasili. 'This is for you to read, my boy! Maybe you understand and like me better.'

Vasili sighed and took the package from his father.

'Goodbye, Father.'

He and Meg arrived at the station in plenty of time to catch the train back to Surrey. They slept most of the way in an empty carriage. Meg skipped and Vasili climbed slowly up the eight steps from the platform into the avenue where they lived. They walked by the petrol pumps and the postal sorting office and then crossed the road to pass the convent next door to Holmwood, their house.

In front of the small drive, and facing a steep road, there was a line of pink and blue hydrangeas. Meg thought of the flowers as soldiers guarding the house. She wondered if Alexis was asleep. She wanted to hear his long story. What was in that envelope he gave to her father?

2

The little bay window

Meg woke the next morning to a feeling of lightness. At last she had met her grandfather. Meg forgot all kinds of things quickly and easily, but if someone or something really struck her, she did remember. Beneath the fresh cotton sheet and paisley silk eiderdown, Meg hugged herself, burrowing down inside her nest before kicking off the bedclothes and jumping out of bed onto the smoky grey carpet.

This evening there was to be a party. Fifty guests had been invited and 'thirty-five are definitely coming, darling,' Jane had told Meg. She and Andrew were allowed to stay up until ten.

After breakfast Meg found Jane in the drawing-room, where she was about to get on with the hoovering. She asked her mother to tell her the story of how she and Andrew were born. Meg often asked this question when she was excited, and even though she knew the story by heart, she never grew tired of it. Sitting down with her mother on the long low sofa covered in pearl grey cotton, she curled up next to her like a cat.

'Well, Meg,' Jane began. 'Once upon a time a little boy called Andrew was born. This little boy took a very, very long time to arrive in the world as he got badly stuck on the way. He huffed and he puffed and he tried and tried to be born. His mother Jane knew there was something wrong but sadly, it was too late, and Andrew's head was damaged.

He was a very weak baby, but he drank his mother's milk and that made him stronger. Andrew's poor head being hurt meant he had epileptic fits. The French name for the fits is *petit mals*, which means "little illnesses".'

'Mum, isn't there some medicine to stop the fits coming?' Maybe this time her mother's answer would be yes.

'There is medicine that helps Andrew not to have so many *petit mals*, but there isn't anything to take them away for good, Meg.'

'And how was I born, Mum? Tell me again.'

'Well, two years and three weeks after Andrew was born, you came along on the 21 June, five months after your grandmother, Hazel, died. I knew you were on your way and, as Dad was at work, I drove myself to the hospital where I parked the car and walked the hundred yards to the entrance, but when I told the nurse you were arriving, she said, "No, dear, not yet. Your baby's not due yet. You'll know when that happens."

'You *were* about to arrive so I stood my ground and said, "But I'm absolutely certain my waters are about to break!" "No, no, dear," the nurse replied, so I walked back to the car and just as I was opening the door my waters broke! When I walked back over to the hospital you and I were rushed to the delivery room and, hey presto, you pushed and swam your way out in under two hours!

'While we were busy getting you born, the young doctor who was helping us, said the birth was so easy the nurse could take over from him, and then he walked over to the big bay window and began singing *This is a lovely way to spend an evening*, like Frank Sinatra. I can remember his voice to this day. Yours was such a very quick and easy birth, Meg. I even asked the young doctor in the middle of it all, if he ever thought of changing jobs and becoming a singer. He laughed and said, "Well, no I haven't, Mrs. Chodak," and he smiled as if he were thinking about the idea. "I'll even have time for a cup of tea before the next delivery," he chuckled. And then you were born, Meg, and no accidents this time.'

This was the story Meg and her mother shared over and over again. She was relieved, elated to hear that she had bounced into the world, but then she would quickly remember the tale of Andrew's head being damaged at birth. His beginning cancelled hers and she froze at the thought. She was fortunate, but her brother being so very unfortunate took the wind out of her sails. Maybe they could swap lives, take turns to be ill. That would be fairer than her forever being well and Andrew forever being sick.

Meg sometimes imagined she and her brother were changelings hatched by fairies and elves and that the *petit mals* were showered on Andrew's head by hobgoblins, who visited his bedroom at night. Andrew was the trembling elf boy and she was his elf sister with a speck in her eye. When Andrew was a little boy he had worn a padded helmet all the time, as he kept falling over. Meg's world was a place full of Andrew's falling body. When he fell she fell too. Where he stumbled, so did she, but without a helmet she fell flat on her face.

Jane returned to her hoovering and Meg ran out of the front door to play. She loved the house and the garden. Holmwood was in a quiet tree-lined avenue. Sometimes Meg thought of the avenue as a large circle with the houses and large gardens caught up inside it. At one point the road climbed a steep hill to arrive at the highest point in the village. There the avenue ended, so it was more a horse-shoe shape than a circle. At the tip of the horseshoe you took a sharp left turn into the main road, which ran down into the village where there was a tight bend right over the railway bridge onto a small row of shops and bus stops.

Meg's house had five bedrooms, a roomy attic and a large two-tiered garden, separated at the top by barbed wire from a small wood owned by the convent next door. Holmwood had an open look, as if it were looking the world in the eye. The house faced the steep stretch of road, which dropped down and then turned up onto Epsom Downs and the racecourse. The line of pink and blue hydrangeas at the front of the house was behind some pretty black chains in loops. Jane tended the flowers, drenching some with tea to turn them blue. This bright June day they were at their height, the big round heads full of tiny petals. Meg stood very still beside the hydrangeas, like a sentinel, touching their heads.

Meg then ran round the side of the house and into the garden. Close by the French windows leading into the drawing-room, stood a large old ash tree with a swing beneath it. The tree was at the edge of the rectangle of the lower lawn and Meg liked to swing high up into the leaves and down again, her stomach dropping with a tingling sensation and catching her breath.

This morning, though, she was full of Alexis and the idea of 'medical gymnastics', which her father didn't like. When she had asked Jane about them at breakfast, her mother told her they were exercises her grandfather gave his patients so they could walk again. Meg stood in the middle of the lawn and then raised her arms above her head before diving into a handstand. She then walked all over the lawn on her hands, counting her steps up to one hundred, two hundred, three hundred. Meg liked to see the garden upside down through her arms. She loved to feel the grass beneath her hands and she hardly ever fell over. The lawn became a huge stage with Meg at its centre.

Today she had a companion. She and Alexis walked on their hands all over the stage. Their movements were perfectly synchronised and, being close in height, they made a very neat couple. Lowering their short legs in tandem, they returned to earth in a single, unhurried move-ment to tumultuous applause. They were a double act. Meg and Alexis swung sparkling hula hoops around and around their waists and hips, to Chubby Checker's Let's Twist Again – 'Round and round and up and down they go again...' – until the hoops dropped around their ankles. Then they took their final bow and danced off the stage hand in hand. They might go on the road, join the gypsies who came with roundabouts and stalls when there was horse-racing on the Downs.

Meg chatted away to herself as she played in the garden. She was an elf, a changeling. Now where had Alexis got to?

****

As Jane had anticipated, around thirty guests arrived for the cheese and wine party that evening. They included Vasili's colleagues from the hospital, along with some of his new friends from London where he was training as a psychoanalyst. There were neighbours – stockbrokers and builders, solicitors and shopkeepers, along with Mr. May, the postman, and the milkman, Mr. Clarke.

Jane told Andrew and Meg that no-one must be left out and that people like the postman were welcome to walk in through the front door and not in at a 'tradesman's entrance'. The idea of a tradesman's entrance made Meg think of dark corners and the alleyway that cut through from the village to the heath, where there were ancient trees, knobbly and gnarled and dwarfish. She and Andrew played houses in little clearings among the trees.

The siblings would run there and back down the alleyway, past the backs of some big gardens. Meg was fearful in the alley like a hound was at her heels. The backs of houses were where bad things happened. A monster might jump out at you.

Meg and Andrew were in the breakfast room, hiding under a table loaded with food and drink. When Andrew was smaller he would line up his Dinky toys, all the colours of a rainbow, on the floor. He placed the vehicles in two long, straight lines each side of himself, the traffic headed in opposite directions – thirty or more cars, trucks, delivery vans, tractors, tanks and lorries one behind the other, which Andrew directed like a policeman on a traffic island. Once Meg waded crash, bang into her brother's lines, but that was unusual. As a rule she never interrupted him when he was playing on his own. She knew that he liked her to stand and watch him. That time, though, Meg kicked the toys in every direction and then picked up the vehicles and threw them all over the light blue lino floor.

The leaves of the large breakfast table were opened out and the table was covered with a starched linen cloth, the colour of damsons, which touched the floor so the guests couldn't see the children underneath. Meg was sitting cross-legged like a nomad, drinking in the scent of the women's perfume, which mingled with the bitter cigarette and cigar smoke swirling all around the room. In the distance she could hear the music her mother was playing on the small record player in the drawing-room – 'One two three o'clock, four o'clock rock – we're gonna rock around that clock tonight, we're gonna rock rock rock in the pale moonlight, we're gonna rock around tonight!' The guests were dancing to Bill Hayley.

Under the table Meg could see the women in their silky New Look dresses with the full skirts and high heeled stilettos, the men in suits, some with waistcoats. All the men wore ties, many loosened at the neck. Some were in V-necked cashmere sweaters like the ones her father wore at the weekends. Andrew was crouched down beside Meg and they were giggling hard, their hands over their mouths so as not to be heard by the adults clustering around the camembert and cheddar and the large cylindrical stilton.

Meg could hear her father discussing the stilton with Mr. May, the postman. 'It is an acquired taste but once you have developed an appreciation, you won't be able to live without it! If you eat some stilton, just a small piece, half an hour before going to bed, you are guaranteed to have an extremely vivid dream. This helps me to get into my unconscious. My wife wakes me in the early hours so I can write the dreams down for my analyst. I think it was G.K. Chesterton who wrote a sonnet to stilton – "this cheese that crumbles to its core".'

Meg was peeking out from underneath the tablecloth,

watching her father wagging his finger at the young postman, as if he were telling him something extremely serious but funny at the same time. Mr. May was smiling. 'Oh, yes, doctor. I've never tasted stilton before but it goes down a treat with the celery I must say. My missus buys cheddar and that's it. I'll watch out for those dreams!'

Mr. May would wink at Meg when he came in for a cup of tea and a piece of cake on Fridays. Her mother would sit down and talk to him about his family and how his children were getting on at their new school. His hair was dark brown and slicked back in the same style as her father's – short back and sides like most grown-up men.

Meg had heard Vasili talking about his 'unconscious' before and now she connected it with eating stilton. This was a word she did not understand but her father often spoke of it, especially over Sunday breakfast and when guests came to dinner. The 'unconscious' must definitely be something to do with food. The word did sound luscious. There were three words Vasili used that she and Andrew shouted to the winds, when the roof of the pale blue Zephyr was down. The words made them laugh and they were easier to say than 'unconscious'.

Meg whispered the words to Andrew who, at eleven, was too big to be under the table. He kept poking Meg in the eye with his elbow, which made her think of Alice. In the White Rabbit's house Alice's body grew so big it took up all the space. She barely squeezed into the house and one foot went up a chimney and kicked Bill, the lizard, so he flew into the air and crashed down outside. Andrew bent over and whispered into Meg's ear. She smelled the medicine on her brother's breath and wanted to be free of him.

From under the table the children began shouting at the tops of their voices, 'Iddy! Ego! Superego! Iddy! Ego! Superego!' They had their own ideas about what the words meant. Ego was an egg of course and the superego, a huge egg. Meg came up with a meaning for the id. It was tomato sauce with lots of little iddy imps jumping around inside the sauce (but you couldn't see them) and when you poured them onto fried egos or superegos and chips, like in the *Wimpy Bar* in Sutton, the iddys were free to go and join their imp relatives, who lived outside the bottle in all kinds of places – in the streets, gardens, attics, cellars, in Tashkent, Bloomsbury, Russia, *The Scala Theatre*, France, England and all over the world.

The siblings squeezed out from under the table and emerged into the room. Some of Vasili's psychiatrist friends were laughing at the children's use of the terms, whilst others looked embarrassed. Vasili smiled at the sight of Meg and Andrew as they stood up together, still giggling. He was talking to Mr. Clarke now, the middle-aged milkman with the sour expression. Meg wondered if her father was talking to him about the egos and the superegos he delivered on his milk cart. Andrew left the room to join the dancers in the drawing-room, but Meg stayed to talk with her father. Mr. Clarke said he was hungry. He would go and get some bread and a slice of cheddar. 'Good honest cheddar and none of this foreign muck, doctor.' Meg wondered what on earth that meant – how could cheese be honest? What was 'foreign muck'? Alexis came from Tashkent so he was foreign but he wasn't 'muck', which was disgusting.

Meg held Vasili's hand. Her father was in one of his happy-sad moods. One moment he was laughing with Mr. May about stilton and the unconscious, and now he was looking a bit lost. She recalled the dream she had told him this morning over breakfast. After finishing her marmalade on toast, she had looked at her father expectantly. Her knee had begun to shake. Vasili was taking ages to finish his bacon and egg but when he did, Meg spoke.

'Dad, please listen. Last night I dreamed I was at the front door but I couldn't open it. I knew that inside there were thousands of people – children and grown ups. My job was to buy food for them all from the village and squeeze it through the letterbox. I made cheese sandwiches and slipped them in. I posted slices of corned beef and ham. The fruit I couldn't post, unless it was grapes, so I left bags full of apples, oranges and bananas outside the door for the people to collect. Mr. Clarke came with the milk and I asked him to bring more in crates as there were so many people to feed!'

Vasili had gazed at her absent-mindedly. 'And what do you make of your dream, Meg?' She didn't make anything of it. She wasn't making up the dream. She wasn't. 'No, darling, I mean why do you think you had the dream?' 'I wanted to help the people inside. I was very frightened, Dad, but I wanted to help them.' Her father had looked vague. Meg suspected this was the wrong answer, as her father said nothing much in reply and simply nodded.

Vasili walked with Meg through the hall and into the dining-room at the front of the house, where a small group of psychiatrists and their wives from the hospital were chatting quietly. Vasili sat down at the baby grand and began to play Beethoven's *Moonlight Sonata*. Meg stood by her father, gazing at the fresh pink begonia on the table beside the piano.

The group of colleagues grew quiet and listened. With his head bent over his hands, Meg sensed that her father was playing with tenderness, whilst faltering over the notes. She was a little embarrassed to witness Vasili stumbling in front of his friends. Finishing abruptly, as if aware that he might have played much better, Vasili sprang up from the piano stool. The stool had once belonged to Alexis and Hazel, along with the three pianos – two grand and one baby grand – which they had given to Vasili when he and Jane married.

Everyone applauded and Meg clapped and clapped. She liked to come upon her father in this calmest of all the rooms in the house. She would often sit by the hearth on the little stool covered in blue velvet as he played, or father and daughter would sit together at the round mahogany dining-table with a bagatelle board in front of them. Meg enjoyed the pinging sound as the stick hit the ivory and her father crying out, 'Bulls eye!' and 'There she goes!' as he hit the balls. As she grew older, Meg associated the game with Beethoven's bagatelles, some of which she learned to play. Her father preferred to tackle dramatic and difficult pieces.

Meg was suddenly filled with a sense that something terrible was about to happen and that she was to blame. Where was Andrew? Was he with her mother? Was he lying down dead on the floor? She should not have left him. She must never leave his side. That was one of the rules she wrote down everyday on a piece of lined exercise paper she had often lost by the end of the day. She got through lots of exercise paper, telling her mother that she needed it to practise her handwriting, when all along she used the paper to write down instructions to herself. She would write, 'Get up', 'Have breakfast', 'Brush teeth', 'Find Andrew' and so on. She knew there was something crazy about this, so she never told anyone. She did worry about where all that paper went. Maybe Mrs. Giles, their cleaner, threw it away.

Meg walked toward the drawing-room, where the jiving had finished. Everyone was assembling for the Sir Roger de Coverley, a folk dance Meg's family and their guests danced every year at the summer party. Adults and a handful of children were lining up down the full stretch of the long and elegant drawing-room, the two full-size grand pianos at each end. Her father and his psychiatrist friends followed Meg into the room.

Vasili walked to the piano furthest from the door. He seemed uncomfortable and tense. Meg knew that faraway look in her father's eyes, which usually meant he was thinking of something else. Meg found it difficult to grasp who exactly her father was and she would often leaf through the photograph albums for pictures of her parents before they got married, searching for clues.

In wedding photos her mother had not changed that much – she was very pretty with a dreaminess in her eyes. She looked shy, even though she loved rock n' roll. Meg did not recognise the painfully thin young man at Jane's side, smiling awkwardly with his eyes scrunched up. In another photograph, taken at Cambridge before he'd met Jane, Vasili was smoking a cigarette and sitting on a wall with his legs tightly crossed. He looked sad, like someone had died.

Vasili sat down at the piano in the alcove where a little bay window, with a built in seat, overlooked an untidy rock garden the previous owners had never finished building.

As the dancers assembled to face each other in two long lines, a colleague of Vasili's sat down at the piano by the French windows. They both raised their hands and nodded to each other down the stretch of floor.

The armchairs and sofa were placed against the walls, so that the dancers had plenty of room. The two men inclined their heads and began to play the jaunty folk tune that accompanied the Roger de Coverley, and down the length and breadth of the room the two lines of dancers were bobbing and nodding, nodding and bobbing, meeting their partner opposite and then backing away.

Meg's uncle had told her that 'de Coverley' was named after a fox running in and out of cover when he was being chased by hounds. Meg wondered if Alexis ran in and out of cover when he ran away from the bandits in Tashkent.

Meg faced Andrew, her dancing partner. She was relieved that he had not fallen down in a fit and was here in front of her. At eleven Andrew promised to be tall. He was already a good two to three inches taller than Meg. He had blue eyes that were always blurry with the medicine he took, and a fine featured face that was sensitive and proud like his father's. His hair was medium brown like Jane's and contrasted with his sister's very dark hair. Andrew could appear both weak and robust in the space of a few seconds.

Every so often he had slight, barely noticeable *petit mals*. Meg liked the sound of the French words. She imagined the *petit mals* petering out gently without a fuss. The fits in real life were very different. They changed everything. They muddled her. Right now, no-one at the party seemed to notice Andrew was having *petit mals*. They just went on dancing. All the guests knew about Andrew's epilepsy but they didn't care. The next thing everyone disappeared and only she and Andrew were in the room, alone with the *petit mals* which had been carried in by the goblins in sacks. Meg checked her imagination sharply and then she was back in the drawing-room dancing the Roger de Coverley with all the guests.

When one pair reached the top of the dancers, close to Vasili's piano in the little bay window, they clasped hands and jigged down the middle of the lines to the other end, with everyone clapping in time to the music. Andrew did not know how to clap in time or dance in step. His rhythm was all wrong and as he jogged towards Meg, his arms flailing about and almost falling over, she thought of the caterpillar in *Alice in Wonderland* when he asks Alice to recite *You are old Father William*.

'In my youth,' father William replied to his son
'I feared it might injure the brain;
But, now that I'm perfectly sure I have none,
Why, I do it again and again.'

Whenever Meg read the poem she worried for Father William and was angry with Alice for getting the poem 'all wrong'. Everyone had a brain and it could be injured badly. It was not a joke. Andrew got things wrong because his brain was damaged and the fits made him think crooked. That's what her mother said. Meg couldn't bear to watch when Andrew tried to stand on his head, as he always fell over and had a *petit mal*. She'd sprint out into the garden to walk on her hands or swing beneath the ash tree, her strong legs pushed out straight before her and then under as she swung back. Up and down she went, wishing the tree would take her into its warm, snug world. There she would be safe. She wouldn't need to worry about Andrew kicking her bedroom door open. He never knocked and came in at all hours, even when she was in bed asleep.

Everyone was clapping as Andrew and Meg jigged down the middle of the lines, with Meg just holding onto her brother. She could hear the applause far in the distance. Suddenly the lines of dancers froze, like in a game of musical statues. Andrew had stopped dead in his tracks and Meg nearly toppled over. Her brother's arms shot out, rigid and jerking, his eyes fixing Meg with a look of terror she knew by heart. She was struck by the hard mechanical rhythm of his jolting, which was strange because in real life Andrew had no rhythm at all.

His arms were out-flung, straight as a die and making short, sharp movements back and forward, as if he were a puppet whose actions had got stuck. Andrew swayed, tipped over and thudded onto the carpet. He was still jerking, but soon his body stilled and his eyes opened.

When Andrew realised what had happened, he blushed a deep and fiery red. He gave Meg a spiteful glance as if to say, 'It's *your* fault, it's all *your* fault!' No-one moved for a split second and then there was Jane rushing to her son's side as Andrew began to stand up. She hugged him but he pulled away from her. Vasili sprang up from the piano and arrived at Andrew's side a second after Jane. They were relieved that this severe *petit mal* had not turned into a *grand mal*. Andrew let his father take his pulse and look into his eyes to see if they were focusing sufficiently. It was alright. The Roger de Coverley could be resumed. Andrew stomped out of the room and Jane followed him. He banged the door behind him so the whole room shook.

Meg was without a partner, so she sat down in one of the armchairs by the fire. Would there never be an end to Andrew's fits that came from nowhere and, if there were no end and no doctor (not even her father or Alexis or her grandmother when she was alive) who could stop them, how could Andrew, how could *she* bear it? If someone asked her to dance she would refuse. How could she join in with everyone carrying on as if nothing had happened?

She looked at the two lines of dancers. With Andrew gone she could see the guests properly. They curtsied and bowed to each other, the dance having arrived at its conclusion with a flourish of notes from Vasili and his colleague. The party guests seemed sad after seeing Andrew having a fit, or was it simply that the dance had finished? After a while they began to laugh and smile and then they were drinking wine, helping themselves to bread and cheese, slicing into the stilton's blue veins. How *could* they? They were pigs. A nursery rhyme came into Meg's head:

> Ring a-ring o'roses
> A pocketful of posies,
> A-tishoo! a-tishoo!
> We all fall down.

Meg walked out of the drawing-room and up to her bedroom. It was not yet nine and this morning she had been excited at being allowed to stay up till ten. She didn't care now. Meg was heavy in her mind. She lay down on her bed and gave in to sleep. Soon she was dreaming. She dreamt that everyone was dancing, not only in the drawing-room, but in every room of the house except for the two bathrooms and Andrew's bare little bedroom with his 'Do Not Disturb' sign on the door.

Everyone she knew was in the house – friends from school, Mr. May, Mr. Clarke and even the gloomy newsagent, Mr. Richards, who caught Meg and Andrew stealing Polos once. He had rapped their knuckles with a ruler in front of everyone in the shop and Vasili was furious. Meg heard him on the phone to Mr. Richards, saying that it was completely wrong to 'hit children' and he had a good mind to cancel his papers.

In her dream everyone's hands were up in the air and there was Andrew in the middle of lines and circles of dancers. Andrew and the dancers were in every room she entered. Her brother was the centre of everyone's gaze. He ignored Meg, who stood in silence on the threshold of every single door. There were lots of Megs in the house. She was everywhere and nowhere. She was frightened. She wanted to spit but she had no spit. Her mouth was dry. She was invisible. And then everyone was falling or on the point of falling. Meg did not fall. She did not move an inch.

After the party Meg's dream kept recurring. Dancing and falling went hand in hand. The dream was like a record stuck in a groove. If you picked up the arm on the turntable and put it back onto the disc, it stuck or jumped out and made a long scratch. The dream ended with everyone falling down for good. There they lay in a great heap. No-one stirred. Andrew was on top of the pile of bodies, twitching. Meg was the only one alive, up on her feet, but then the scene changed in a flash and there was Alexis, a boy of fourteen, running away from the line of bodies on the Russian plain. She could not see him for dust.

****

The following evening Meg overheard her parents talking about making an appointment for Andrew at the National Hospital. She recalled the large building in Bloomsbury her father had pointed out to her. That night Meg dreamt that she and Andrew were in the breakfast room. This was a dream she'd had before. They were very small children, almost babies, and Andrew was clenching his fists so hard, the knuckles went white. Meg gazed at the fierceness in her brother's unfocused eyes, and then his arms shot out as if he was going to hug her. She waited with growing impatience for the *petit mals* to pass. Holding her breath she counted the twenty-eight seconds the little fits took. For the duration she stood there, holding a red lorry aloft in her fist. She did not think of the sheep clambering over the stiles on her Uncle Peter's farm. She just kept counting, one, two, three until Andrew returned from the place of bad magic in his head which no-one, not even her mother and father, had ever visited. She and Andrew and the elves and the goblins alone knew this place and it was theirs. No-one else must enter.

In her dream Meg suddenly found herself in a little room with turquoise walls. The air was sweet and fresh. She began to chant a name that brought more comfort than she could tell. Alexis, Alexis, Alexis. His name was like kisses, one after the other, lots of little crosses she tucked away inside the corners of her mind.

3

The divining-rod scar

1962

The thought of Alexis buoyed Meg up through the long winter months. Andrew went for his appointment at the National Hospital, but all the doctors could do was increase the amount of pills he took. They were sorry, but there was really nothing more to be done. In the spring of the following year Andrew began his first term at a boarding school in Sussex. Over the years he had attended special schools in the local area intermittently, whenever his epilepsy wasn't too severe. The school in Sussex was, Jane told Meg, for children like Andrew who needed a different kind of education. Andrew couldn't go to an ordinary school because his epilepsy made it very difficult for him to concentrate.

Meg was glad that Andrew was getting some help and also secretly pleased that he was going away. He might return cured. She wondered what his new school was like. Her parents didn't take her there in his first term, as he needed to settle in. Jane told Meg Andrew would be gardening and acting in plays and painting and spending a lot of time in the open air. 'He might feel more free,' Meg heard her father say over the phone to one of his doctor friends. There would be lots of music for him to express himself. Meg wondered a great deal about Andrew's special school.

She was surprised to find that she missed her brother badly. She had grown used to being with Andrew in the evenings and at weekends. School friends rarely came for tea now as Meg kept her distance. She hated friends coming to the house, when Andrew would burst into her bedroom and have *petit mals* in front of them. She dreaded the look of horror and embarrassment on their face. In his absence, though, Meg felt bereft. Andrew's suddenness, his fits, were woven into her being and, even if she liked the quietness when he was gone, she was not used to it. Silences were meant to be broken and rooms were made to be broken into.

When Andrew returned in the spring holidays Meg was very glad to see him. He was still having lots of fits, but he seemed happier. By contrast, Meg had shrunk into herself. She looked slight and wary and had a glazed look in her eyes. The speck in the left eye was less noticeable. Her small body was tense and her expression guarded.

One Sunday, after an early lunch, Meg entered the drawing-room and saw her mother sitting on the window seat in the bay, weaving her latest tapestry. Jane was working on a cover for one of the three piano stools. Meg loved to come upon her mother sewing and she sat down next to Jane, contemplating the picture that was almost finished. The spray of flowers warmed her – crimson and plum, azure blue and gold, and leaves in various shades of green.

She found it difficult, though, to sit still for any length of time and after five minutes Meg went outside through the French windows, which were open as the weather was mild. She ran around to the side of the house and tapped on the little bay window. Turning her head, Jane smiled to see Meg waving at her. Directly opposite the window there was the unfinished rock garden.

Meg climbed over the muddle of stones and long grasses that were growing wild. It was more a heap of haphazard rubble than a garden. She then hoisted herself up into a hollow, a small niche beneath a canopy of thorny shrubs.

Through the bay window she could see her mother's head bent over the tapestry and her father sitting at the piano. Andrew was nowhere to be seen.

Meg liked this cramped and inaccessible place. Tiny, one of the family's four cats, jumped over the rocks and leapt up into Meg's lap. She was an elegant and sleek cat with a little white dot on her throat. It was hard to believe she was the mother of the big tom, Flash, who was black with a dramatic white splash on his throat. Tiny's mother, Kitty, was a pretty tabby and Big Uncle made the fourth. He was a stout black cat, unrelated to the others, and would disappear for long stretches, days at a time, before he turned up again looking more handsome than ever.

Meg loved the cats and their wariness, their independent ways. She admired their unpredictability. She could hear the faint notes of the slow Chopin prelude her father was playing and was reminded of the cats' beauty and of their sadness. Cats were never happy like busy, barking dogs. They could be pleased and snug and lovely to touch, but they slinked and darted and snoozed and turned away.

With Tiny in her lap, Meg half dozed for ten minutes or so, when she was woken suddenly by Andrew's voice shouting from the top of the garden, 'Meg! Meg! Where are you?' She jumped down from her niche and clambered back over the stones. Running inside, she leapt up the stairs and into her bedroom, where she looked out of the window that faced the garden. The branches and leaves of the ash tree filled the pane.

Meg guessed Andrew was in the shed, which was tucked away in the left hand corner of the upper tier of the garden, close by the bluebell wood. Andrew kept lots of tools in the shed – hammers, saws, chisels and nails. He made shelves and boxes for his mother to use and carved little wooden animals, cats and dogs and lions and camels, as ornaments for the house. Meg worried he would cut off his arm or leg if he had a fit, or he might fall and hurt his head on the saw's jagged edge and blood would pour down his face and all over his shirt.

Meg contemplated herself in the cheval mirror. She loved her light green pedal pushers and their jauntiness, the summery texture of the soft cotton. She stuck her tongue out at herself and stood very still and straight, waiting a few seconds before flinging out her arms, rigid and jerking.

She was attempting to imitate Andrew having a fit, but this idea was bound up with thinking she might actually induce a real fit. She threw herself down onto the floor, landing hard on her face. There she thrashed about before becoming inert. The only movement in her body was her mouth chomping. She couldn't bring herself to bite her tongue, like Andrew did when he had a big fit. She had never seen him having a *grand mal*.

'Andrew hardly ever has a *grand mal*, darling, and if he does he has it in bed when he wakes up or when he's falling asleep.' Her mother had learned how to time her own sleep so that she woke every couple of hours. She would then go and check to see if Andrew was alright. Her father asked Jane to wake him at the same time, so that he could make notes on his dreams in an exercise book while they were in mid-flow. Otherwise he would forget them. Meg imagined her mother must be very tired, getting up in the night to wake Andrew and her father, but she did love the idea of her father writing about his dreams. She wished her mother would wake her and then she could write down her dreams in an exercise book.

'Meg, Meg, come here! Meg, Meg!'

Her brother's voice was urgent, staccato. It went right through her. Wherever Andrew was, though, and whatever she might be doing at the time, she was under oath to be at his side. She'd make herself do whatever he wanted. Meg rolled over onto her side with her back to the window. She held her breath and began counting. Maybe she could have a fit that way. Ten, twenty, thirty, forty, fifty seconds, a whole minute. When she could hold it no longer, she blew out a long breath and relaxed. She was disappointed. She never would have epilepsy like Andrew, but at every opportunity she tested herself. Turning over onto her back, Meg gazed up at the magnolia ceiling. Why did she want to have a fit? She was crazy.

****

The small, ancient wood at the top of the garden was on the other side of the barbed wire, which separated the garden from the convent grounds. Behind the wire there was a dense and swaying mass of bluebells. The heads of the little bell-shaped flowers were bent toward the ground. Meg drank in the mild spring air. She walked slowly past the ash tree and the swing in its boughs, glancing at the garden bench beneath the tree. Sometimes Meg spent up to an hour sitting on the bench, playing bagatelle or solitaire. Mostly, though, she swung high up into the tree, an elf child glimpsing bits of sun and blue sky. As she swung higher and higher, her brother's *petit mals* fluttered around her like small and delicate birds. The French words reminded Meg of the wild strawberries that grew in among the shrubs and at the foot of the trees in the wood. Pretty *petit mals*.

The garden was divided by two banks, with red brick steps in the middle connecting the upper and lower stretches of grass. The lower lawn Jane or Vasili mowed regularly to keep it smooth. Meg skipped up the steps, enjoying the reassuring solidity of the red brick. On the top tier the grass was long and tangled with wildflowers.

Andrew was waiting for Meg beside the barbed wire, which she lifted for him to squeeze through. Being much smaller, she managed to climb in between the wire without his help. The wood was a special place where Meg became mysterious, silent and still. The ancient trees and the blue-bells were full of old magic. Meg was in Narnia. The trees sheltered the hard knot of love she bore Andrew. She loved him more than anyone, much more than her mother, her father and Alexis.

In the wood the siblings had carved their initials into one of the larger trees: AC loves MC, Andrew Chodak loves Meg Chodak. They nicked their flesh with Andrew's little penknife and mingled bloods. Meg would do anything for her brother in the wood and in the past year her love and loyalty had been tested. Andrew was almost twelve and Meg not quite ten. Last summer they had kissed in the wood quite a lot, but Meg did not like to think of that. The smell of the medicine on her brother's breath made her nauseous, but she managed to hold back the retching. The kisses were Andrew's idea and Meg was curious.

There was no tenderness, no affection in Andrew's kisses. Instead, there was angry passion that drove him to press his sister much too hard against the back of a tree. She had little idea of what lay behind her brother's urgency. Andrew was furious or ecstatic in a way that reminded her of fireworks. There was nothing but his fury and his ecstasy. Meg went numb all over. She counted the seconds. She believed the bluebell wood cradled her.

When Andrew kissed her, Meg imagined the two of them living in a little house of their own in the woods. The fits would be refused entry, even if they knocked and banged and threatened to break the house down. She would open the letter box and with her water pistol she would squirt tomato sauce and vinegar at the monsters. The sauce was full of little iddys dancing about and they would jump on top of the fits, nipping and biting them. 'Leave us alone. You just leave us alone!' she'd shout.

She and Andrew were Hansel and Gretel and the witch was the bad epileptic magic they bundled into the piping hot oven. They were babes in the wood in among the bluebells, which their mother said were lovelier than hyacinths, more delicate and less showy. Meg and her brother had walked through the back of the wardrobe into the woods in Narnia.

Today Meg and Andrew did not kiss. Andrew climbed the trees and ran up and down the length of the small wood, frantically happy. The sunshine was filtering through the trees and lit upon a young girl, a novice from the convent, who was on her knees beside one of the trees at the far edge of the wood. Her eyes were closed, her palms pressed together and her head bent in prayer. Meg, who was standing near the barbed wire, heard the low, murmuring voice but she could not make out the words.

Andrew rushed up to Meg. 'Look, Meg, look at the lady!' They began giggling and then they were rolling over and over in among the bluebells, Andrew pinching Meg very hard. Meg grew frightened of the woman in the strange black clothes that almost covered her whole body, with only her face showing. She wasn't scared of nuns. It was just that she had never seen one in the wood before.

The novice stood up and turned in the children's direction, smiling at them before she walked away toward the convent. She didn't tell them off and Meg felt disappointed, let down. The nun's smile had warmed her, like she was saying everything will be alright, children. I live in a house full of nuns. Meg liked the sound of the word. Maybe she could be a nun when she grew up. She could stay near the bluebell wood for ever and they would have a special room for Andrew where he could get better.

As Meg was climbing back into the garden, she slipped and the barbed wire tore into her left wrist, blood splashing all over her arm and staining her light blue shirt. She cried as she ran and stumbled behind Andrew, who was leaping through the long grass and down the banks, his feet barely touching ground. 'Emergency! Emergency!' he shouted as he raced into the kitchen where Jane was cooking chicken in white sauce for dinner that evening.

Her mother wound a clean dishcloth tight around Meg's wrist and Vasili walked her to the doctor, who lived a few houses away from Holmwood. Meg went very quiet in the consulting room and only gulped as the doctor's needle pierced the thin white skin that had been torn. The pain was searing. 'No need for an anesthetic,' said the young doctor, 'you shouldn't go squeezing through barbed wire to trespass on convent property! You are a very lucky girl not to have hit an artery.'

Yes, she was very fortunate. Meg did not know what an 'artery' was but believed she was blessed. She was silent that evening when Jane came to kiss her goodnight. 'It's bound to hurt, darling, but it'll be all better very soon. I know I said you might play in the wood. The nuns did say it was alright, but you'd better not go there for the time being.'

The next morning Andrew told Meg they were going up to the bluebell wood again but not to tell their mother. He was carrying two big baskets and gave Meg some tattered old sheets to carry. With her wrist bandaged and throbbing, and with the bundle of bedclothes in her arms, Meg followed Andrew and squeezed through the wire as usual.

'We're picking all the bluebells, Meg, to give to Mum!' Andrew shouted at her.

They cut through every single stalk they could see, Andrew with his sheaf knife and Meg with kitchen scissors, and soon the thick carpet of bluebells was reduced to mushy green stubble. Andrew counted the flowers, one after another up to three hundred and eight. Meg picked them nervously, touching her wrist every so often to test how much it hurt. The pain was sharp and she felt nauseous.

She was worried that Andrew's idea of cutting down the bluebells was against the law and that they would get into trouble with the police. Was it alright or wasn't it? She wasn't sure. Her mother had said *not* to pick them as they wouldn't grow again, but maybe it didn't matter. Meg liked the fact that Andrew counted the flowers. They picked every single bluebell until there were none left.

Andrew was always counting things. Her father said that this didn't matter as counting helped Andrew. Some days he counted every single thing in the house and that took him a long time. Meg hoped he might never arrive at an end of the counting, but then guilt consumed her. When they had filled the two baskets with flowers, they threw the rest, their heads heavy and sticky with sap and dew, onto the old bed sheets.

Andrew kept grinning at Meg. Did he know what they were doing was wrong? Meg wondered. She wasn't sure. Her mother did love the bluebells.

They carried the baskets and sheets through the French windows into the drawing-room. The sheets were drenched and sagging with the weight of the flowers. Jane was hoovering upstairs, so Andrew and Meg went into the kitchen and collected all the vases they could find inside and on the top of a large cupboard – vases of every shape, size and colour in cut glass, pottery and china, which they filled with water from the kitchen tap. They crammed the containers with the bluebells. Meg noticed that the flowers were drooping more than ever. They placed the vases in the hallway, the drawing-room, the dining-room, the breakfast room, the kitchen and the downstairs toilet beneath the stairs. The whole of the ground floor smelled of mild, dewy honey.

Andrew and Meg waited for their mother in the drawing-room. 'Don't call Mum. I want it to be a big surprise. Don't say anything, Meg.' Andrew held his finger to his mouth in a shushing gesture. When Jane walked in, she saw the children standing by the grand piano in the bay. On top of the piano, next to a potted begonia, there were several vases filled with bluebells. Taking in at a glance the many containers on the tables and beside the hearth, she gasped, crying out in exasperation. Meg could see her mother was on the verge of tears.

'I told you not to pick the bluebells, not ever! They won't grow again. The bluebells in the wood are very, very precious. They won't grow again!'

Meg began to cry and Andrew kicked the French windows open with his boots, which left a dent and a dirty mark. He might have shattered the pane and for a brief moment Meg saw fear in her mother's blue eyes. She had never seen her brother look so angry before. Outside Andrew zoomed around the garden, shouting swear words to the sky. Meg felt embarrassed for him.

First he was a plane and next a racing car. Round and round he went, up and down the banks and steps, skidding to a halt in the middle of the lower lawn (as if he had chosen that very spot) and then his arms shot out. Nothing mattered now. The bluebells were nothing and the world stood still in its tracks. Jane ran out into the garden with Meg close behind her. The fits came to an end and Andrew returned from the land of goblins.

Whatever came before and after the bluebells was not worth thinking about in the face of Andrew's illness. When the *petit mals* were over, Meg wanted badly to clap but she didn't as that was how the game went. Everyone must pretend nothing happened or Andrew would be furious. She knew this was her brother's wish. Her right knee began to shake.

One of Meg's teachers, the youngest in the school who taught English, had told Meg the story of Houdini last term. Houdini was the man who could escape from anything, even when he was thrown, tied up in chains, into a deep river and almost drowned. At last he would break free and then his head would appear above the water and he'd shout with triumph and wave and everyone clapped. Meg was entranced by the story and believed that Andrew was like Houdini. He was what her teacher called 'an escape artist'.

Meg recalled the story now and touched her aching wrist. She and Andrew and Alexis were escape artists. Her destiny was bound up with her brother's and her grandfather's. Thinking about it all was confusing, tiring. What did it mean to be lucky or unlucky? How could you tell who was the lucky one? She felt like her head would explode with all these thoughts.

When she was a little older, Meg noticed that the scar on

her left wrist resembled a divining rod, with its straight line forking into two. The wire had just missed an artery, so the divining rod scar became her lucky scar, reminding her of the bluebell wood. She was a dryad and might die in the arms of a tree. The trunk would absorb her body and her spirit. She hugged the secret of the wood close to herself. After the bluebells she and Andrew visited the wood, but less. Meg missed the quietness.

The memory of that silent, holy place of her childhood would, through later years, continue to nourish her dreams. Violets and wood strawberries at the roots of trees. To her great surprise the bluebells did return the following spring and Meg wanted to run and tell her mother, 'Look, the bluebells have grown again! You said they wouldn't but they did!' She kept their return to herself, though. In the scale of things the fact of their reappearance was unimportant.

Meg counted her blessings. There was the wood, the divining-rod scar on her wrist and the black speck in her left eye. Someone said the speck was bewitching but that didn't sound right. Green eyes to Andrew's blurry blue. Meg in adulthood cradled Andrew, her child, in the wood of her dreams. His eyes began to clear and the mist dissolved. She was a woman grown wise. She could kiss away the *petit mals* upon the lightest breeze. The earth beneath her feet might absorb those disarming *petit mals*; they would come to no harm.

****

A few weeks later, after Meg's wrist had healed, Jane took them swimming in Epsom. Meg was a good swimmer. She had learned to swim when she was five. Having swum half-way down the pool she watched her brother from the water. Andrew stood at the edge of the twenty foot diving board, the highest of the four boards. He was about to jump (he never dived) when suddenly his body teetered and shook in a series of *petit mals*. The attendants knew Andrew by now and allowed Jane to watch her son from the side of the pool, instead of from the gallery with the other parents.

In her red bubble bathing costume and pink swimming hat, Meg was treading water in the middle of the pool. Even though the thin rubber hat covered her ears, the huge echoing noise was deafening. The shouting and the splashing ricocheted and bounced off the walls into Meg's ears. Boys were racing and jumping and diving, slicking back their wet hair all around her, but she had eyes for her brother alone, the brave boy who was trembling way up there on the top board. Her father had told her that Andrew's brain knew when he was in danger, so he could have a fit and keep his balance.

After the *petit mals* had passed, Andrew leapt into the air, holding his nose. You might have heard a pin drop in the silence as Meg and her mother watched Andrew fall. He fell and fell through the air, shrieking, jerking mid-air in another *petit mal* before crashing down into the water. Meg and Jane waited. Meg held her breath and counted – one, two, three, four, five, six, seven – and there was Andrew's head bobbing up, his arms flailing about in delight. He threw back his head and doggy-paddled to the side of the pool in frantic uncoordinated movements. Having hauled himself up he skidded and rushed back up the steps to have another go.

Meg swam to the side of the pool and held onto the rail. She did not look up at the board as Andrew jumped for the second time, turning instead toward the shallow end, launching out into the pool. She began to enjoy her favourite stroke, the breaststroke, her head rising and falling in barely perceptible movements, keeping perfect time with her breath which was regular and unerring. She admired her own poise which kept despair at bay. Meg swam with a sense of correctness and yet she envied Andrew his never-say-die leap into the air, his unashamed doggy paddle (the only stroke he had ever been able to learn), his pure joy. Meg's breaststroke did not involve any furious splashing. She raised her head slightly, her green eyes level with the water.

Meg could swim long distances. Only last week she swam twenty-five lengths of this big pool, without even stopping to hold the rails at either end. She never tired of the elegant motion that was hers and hers alone.

In the pool Meg felt grown up, but at school she was a child who found it very hard to concentrate, so she daydreamed a lot of the time. She managed to get by, got her homework done, because she was clever and her mother was encouraging. She even excelled in some subjects, English especially. In that subject she was not required to memorise anything. She liked reading and writing stories. She liked running around the playground, shouting words and sentences to the winds. None of what she did at school, though, felt real to her, apart from the stories she took to her bed, recalling them as she was about to drift off to sleep and then they carried on in her dreams.

At school Meg soon realised that having a brother who shuddered in *petit mals* pretty well all of the time, was odd, weird. Her friends teased her about her 'batty brother' and tapped their heads. Batty. 'Your brother's batty, Meg.' When she told them that her father took all the padded cells out of his hospital, they thought he was 'batty' too and tapped their heads again. 'Your Dad's batty, Meg,' they said.

She hated the girls for this teasing and she hated her brother for having fits and her father for his mad patients. Hatred was a secret she pushed deep down inside herself. When she went to the girls' houses she was someone else, a little girl who enjoyed the ordinariness of homes uninterrupted by fits. The fathers worked in banks or in the stock market and they were very unlike Vasili. They never discussed their dreams. The mothers were quite like Jane, only they were not so worried.

Meg read certain books over and over again. She first read *The Lion, The Witch & The Wardrobe* when she was seven and ever since that first journey into Narnia, she had walked, without fail, through her wardrobe every morning, to find snow crunching beneath her feet. She would find herself inside the wood beside the lamp post. When she was really fed up with the girls at school, Meg imagined herself as the White Witch. She would wave her wand and turn the girls to stone and they would be frozen forever, along with their idiotic grins. She would walk around their statues, sticking her tongue out at them.

The idea of being turned to stone was one Meg kept returning to in her thoughts. When she and her parents were sitting at a meal, Andrew's knife and fork would suddenly fly out of his hands and clatter to the ground. All eyes would be on him as the three of them waited, frozen, their knives and forks poised in mid-air, for the fit to pass. When it ended no-one said a word.

4

The old sea chest

1992

Meg sat back in the armchair. Here she was in her twenty-sixth residence, since leaving home at eighteen. In her early forties, this was the first flat she felt at home in and could call her own. Her father's legacy had enabled her to buy the property at the beginning of last year.

Meg had risen early to get on with the hard work of thinking about her history. She had been attempting to come to terms with her feelings about Andrew, having undergone a course of analytic psychotherapy. The middle part of her life, spent at so many addresses, was still a hazy blur, but the memories of her early childhood and adolescence were beginning to take a more definite shape.

She noticed that her recollections often took the form of strong and sudden bursts of vitality and colour. Revisiting the ballet, the visit to Alexis, the party and the bluebell wood behind barbed wire had preoccupied her for the past few days.

This child, Meg, had appealed to Alexis, her grandfather, that exotic stranger whose presence had so dazzled and delighted her at that one and only meeting. She had called up his image whenever she had needed to believe in something that could wish away Andrew's illness and her guilt. Meg thought of herself as a rational person, but back then she had believed absolutely in Alexis and the bluebell wood. She had conjured spirits and elves from the air. She had walked through the back of her wardrobe. Where was Andrew now? Meg knew he was long gone, but he continued to live on in her memory and in her imagination. Wherever she went, Andrew was beside her. They had sworn to be there for each other to the death.

Twenty-six addresses. Meg had rented rooms, bedsits and flats throughout London, south, north, east and west. Once she had lived for over a year (a record) in a tower block in Stockwell. The tall building swayed in strong winds and the lifts broke down every other day. She had lived here by the common, in this late Victorian house, for two years now (another record).

The urge to move on was never far off and Meg knew that the longer she stayed in this place, the harder it would be to summon the energy to remain. And yet she was here for the time being. Meg stretched her legs. It was the summer holiday and there was the rest of June and the whole of July and August, in which she might continue with this work before beginning some postgraduate research at a college in Bloomsbury. Her father's legacy had enabled her to pay the fees and she had also secured a grant, on the basis of some preliminary findings in the field of women's poetry.

She had even begun writing poetry herself, short lyrics mostly, which were dreamlike, wistful. In her thirties she had been awarded a BA after three years at a university on the south coast, yet Meg was amazed she had managed to get the degree at all. For much of her life, before and after university, she had worked as a temporary secretary, which had felt more real to her than the life of a student.

Despite the research, the large stretch of common, the many large and mature trees she could see from her top floor window, life still felt unreal and insubstantial. Meg shifted in her chair. She had half-listened to someone on the radio yesterday, who said that 'time' was the most 'precious gift you might give anyone.'

For the past week she had gone out little. Sometimes she went for a drink with Elaine and Robert, a couple who lived on the ground floor, but they were away on a walking tour on the Scottish borders and Meg luxuriated in being solitary. Here she was, sitting in her split-level apartment. If you stood in the hallway, the hub of the flat, and then looked up the stairs that led into the sitting-room, and down the stairs to the front door, and then behind you to where the bedroom and bathroom were tucked away, possibilities suggested themselves.

There was an illusion of space and a pleasing sense that you were standing at a place where many paths might meet. Meg liked to stand at the top of the stairs in the doorway to her sitting-room, and then gaze down at the hub and the vista opening up. A tall fig tree stood in the hall and stretched toward a skylight. The previous owners had left her the tree when she moved in, and Meg could not imagine the flat without it. She would reach up above the door, as if mimicking the tree in its growth toward the light.

Meg yawned. What time was it? Half past eight. She made herself some coffee and for a while sat gazing out at the common, where people were walking toward the underground and bus stops on their way to work, the roads that crossed the common busy with traffic.

She decided to give herself and Andrew a rest for now and turn her mind to something else. There were the two boxes of her father's papers, which she had only just begun to sort through. These were filled with letters and papers and a handful of very old photographs. Meg kept the boxes in an old sea chest in her kitchen, which had travelled with her over the last decade. The dealer in the North London antique shop told her it was old pine and would probably have belonged to a sea captain in the eighteenth century.

Along with the boxes, the chest held three opera scores by Benjamin Britten, signed by the composer, thanking his dear friend, Dr. Chodak, for all 'his help at Aldeburgh' –

the first Aldeburgh festival her grandfather had helped organise. There were also bundles of her father's piano sheets and music books, mostly of Beethoven, Chopin and Bach.

After eating, Meg went into the kitchen to open the chest. She wasn't planning any systematic sorting of her father's papers and enjoyed the idea of dipping in at random. Pulling out some bundles of letters, she set them aside and delved deeper. There were letters and more letters and then her eye was caught by a large brown envelope that was wedged tight under one of the flaps at the bottom of the box. FOR VASILI was written on the front. Meg had a sudden sense of keen déjà vu. The envelope looked very familiar. Her heart began thumping as she drew out a manuscript typed on loose leaves of thin green paper. It was a carbon copy with a few typos still showing through.

A single piece of white writing paper sat on top of the manuscript and on this Meg read, 'This is for you, Vasili. It is the story of my life, our life which Hazel and I, we write for you. Maybe you like me better after you read it. Your mother is the true author and I tell her the stories. We write it over many, many years – ten, twenty or more. Sometimes we leave it for a long time and then we start writing again. Your mother, she kept adding bits and pieces and writing some parts again. I am sorry I only give it to you now. Please tell the story to Jane and Meg as well, when she is old enough to understand. With all my love, Father.' Alexis had signed his name once above the handwritten date, May 31 1961, the year Meg had visited her grandfather.

Meg felt as if she had dived to the bottom of an ocean, where an old ship had lain for centuries. She swam into the wreck and came upon some treasure in an oilskin packet and then emerged, her head breaking through the waves.

Half past nine. Meg poured herself another cup of coffee and began to read.

5

Cor-a-cle

1904

A boy of fourteen was sitting at midday in the shade of a solitary tree at the edge of a wide expanse of farmland on the outskirts of Tashkent. People who had lived in the region for centuries before the Russians came, called it the 'czarist city'. The boy's family had moved here from St. Petersburg in the 1880s just before he was born. He was counting with his eyes closed as he was playing hide and seek with his little sister, Tatyana, who at three years old was the youngest of his siblings. He was the eldest of six – two boys and four girls, and almost a man his father said. His family were Chodaks – the Uzbek word for 'white gentlemen' or 'White Russians'.

The Uzbeks lived in the old town with the Persians and Kirghiz and Tartars and Jews and Hindus and gypsies and the Sarts, 'who are city nomads,' the boy's father often told him. They come and go, the Sarts, he said, but they like our city the best. His father also told him that 'we Russians have come to share our culture and learning with the peoples of Tashkent.'

Alexis had met Tsar Nicholas II, once when he was a baby and again when he and his father visited St. Petersburg in 1902. That was when he was twelve and the Tsar had commented on his small stature. In the Tsar's presence Alexis had longed with tremendous fervor to grow tall as the spire on the new Russian cathedral in Tashkent, where he and his family worshipped every Sunday, but he never did.

Here on the farm, playing with Tati, Alexis imagined a bright future.

'I'm coming!' he shouted as he leapt up, feeling comfortable and free in his loose working knickerbockers and strong boots. Alexis ran in the direction of the sheds for the goats and hens, where he found Tati crouched down in some small bushes, barely hidden at all and giggling with delight, as her brother caught her up in his arms.

This morning he and Tati had helped to milk the cows and goats and collect the eggs. There were plenty of farmhands to do this but as Alexis told an uncomprehending Tati, 'Father said we should all pitch in as well. The serfs are emancipated now and we must not expect them to do all the work on the farm.' Alexis was proud of his father. He was a liberal. He paid the serfs money and gave them time to rest during the day. His father's kind words meant a lot to Alexis.

Every day Alexis woke early, washed and dressed quickly to work on the farm, before returning for a breakfast of black bread and tea from the samovar, fresh cucumbers and dumplings, and a glass of the bittersweet kvass he loved. His father would clap Alexis on the shoulder, saying, 'My son, you are a true Russian and no lazy Oblomov slug-a-bed!'

Alexis was crawling on the ground with Tati on his back geeing him up, when his eye was caught by a sudden flash of green. He looked up and saw the green, red and blue shirts of some men on horses, strangers he had not laid eyes on before. They were a few yards away from where he had found Tati by the sheds and they were dressed in billowing tunics, with large belts slung around their hips. Their hair was unkempt and there was a hard, glittering look in their eyes.

Alexis knew about insurrectionists against the Russians – Uzbeks, pan-Turkics and Sufis, and very recently

Bolsheviks, who wanted to foment (a word Alexis had learned last week) a revolution against the Tsar. The Russian workers built the railway in the eighties and it was those men who had fostered the spirit of Bolshevism in the region, his father said. 'But,' he had continued, 'they are fellow Russians, Lexi, and we must welcome them into our homes and talk with them about our liberal ideas. Imperial families such as ours are in Central Asia to keep the rule of law.'

Behind the three men on horses (who were Central Asian, of one tribe or another, he could not tell which) Alexis saw his mother and father and all his siblings moving, stumbling towards him with two more men urging them on with the butt of their guns. Alexis's family had been rounded up, corralled and yet they were walking with dignity.

His sister, Sophia, aged eleven, looked terrified but in a quiet way. Tears ran down her cheeks and she was moaning soft and low. She was praying very hard, Alexis felt sure, to their good Orthodox God. The little ones, Katerina and Mary and Nicholas, who were four, five and six years old, seemed dazed and frightened but unaware of what was going on and where they were being led. The men had surprised the family in the dacha which was a few hundred yards away from the sheds where Alexis and Tati were playing.

Brandishing their guns and swords and knives, they had searched the house and dragged the family outside. When one of the men asked if there were any more brothers and sisters, Katerina told him, 'Yes, there are Lexi and Tati and they're playing hide and seek. They are at their favourite place with the goats,' she said, pointing in the direction of the shed.

The three men on horses, and the two marshalling the family, moved on out into the open plain, the rich fertile soil watered by the Chimgan river and farmed by Russian families for the past few decades. Alexis held Tati in his arms and Katerina clung onto one of his legs, whimpering.

Their mother was soothing Sophia whilst Mary and Nicholas walked on either side of their father.

One of the men, who seemed to strut in his saddle, was older than the rest, a man of forty or so with blonde, matted hair. He shouted to the family in a mixture of Uzbek and Russian, 'Stand in a line, Russian filth, one by the other – quick! We have come to take back our land from you Russian vermin!' He spat on the ground. The other men had death in their cold eyes. Alexis could not understand why he felt so calm.

He stood straight, wishing to be tall and courageous in the face of the brigands. He felt a hand on his shoulder and turned to see that his mother, Catherine, was at his side. She must be with her first-born at this hour. Alexis still held Tati and his mother was now cradling Mary close to her breast. His father, Alexander, was carrying Nicholas whilst Sophia (composed now) cradled her little sister Katerina.

'Put the children down!' the blonde man shouted.

Five men stood in a line. A mother, father, two sons and four daughters also stood in a line. The lines faced each other. They might have been at a dance, only there would need to be three more men on their side so everyone had partners. They'd jig forward and back, back and forward, and then join hands and raise them in the air, like the family did after their evening meal when his father sang Russian folk songs and he, as the eldest, played the balalaika, an instrument passed down through his family for centuries. The couple at the end of the lines would jig down the middle with everyone clapping.

Alexis felt he should have been praying in these last seconds of life and here he was imagining a dance in the face of a firing squad. His mother slumped dead as a bullet hit her clean through the head and Tati's little body was blown apart. They could not have suffered. Alexis listened to his father's deep moans until another bullet silenced him. He heard a little whimpering from Sophia but they shot her again as well. All went quiet and Alexis held his breath. It felt like forever before anyone moved. The men jumped up onto their strong Uzbek horses and shouted, guns raised to the sky, and then they were gone. Was he dead or alive? Alexis had curled himself up in a ball beneath the weight of his mother's body, which shielded him as she fell.

He stayed in this position for what seemed like hours. It was five minutes or less. No time to take stock. No time. He heaved himself up from beneath his mother's body and laid her gently on her back. He studied her face. She was calm, surprised in death. The single hole in her head was neat. There was little blood and her dear face looked the same as before the men came. The rest of his family Alexis could not bear to contemplate, although he did steal one glance at the body, the blood and the guts, of his father, who had been blasted through the stomach and heart. He dared not look at his face.

Alexis could feel his own heart thumping like explosions inside his small sturdy frame. His littleness had saved him. His mother had protected him from the bullets. The men did not notice Alexis curled up beneath her, or if they did, thought him dead. All in a line they had fallen like a deck of cards. Like in *Alice in Wonderland*, Alexis thought – that was his favourite children's book in English, which his mother read to him when he was a boy. Like a deck of cards. One beside another and another and another on either side of him. Was he the joker in the pack or the ace?

Alexis walked away from his family and crouched for another five minutes or so beneath a tree that was close to the dacha. When Alexis entered his large home with its many windows (a gift from the Tsar) he found the bodies of the six servants on the floor of the kitchen, the walls spattered with blood. They were all dead and lying or sitting in pools of dark blood. They had all fallen down. All fall down. That English nursery rhyme his mother had taught her family. Alexis and his siblings would join hands and in a circle they danced and sang:

Ring a-ring o'roses
A pocketful of posies
A-tishoo! a-tishoo!
We all fall down.

No time for nursery rhymes. He must run for cover, be sharp and keep his wits about him.

Alexis hid in one of the cowsheds until nightfall, afraid that the men might return or a Russian friend of the family would call and take him to safety. He did not want to be rescued. He longed to be anywhere but here. Alexis knew he had to make his way in the world alone now. He must leave Russia for good. He'd go to London, that great city his mother – his mother – visited once when she was a girl. 'It is a tremendous place, Lexi – with lots of green parks and a great square named after the battle Admiral Nelson fought against the French – the magnificent hero your father admires so much! It is not so cold as Russia but there is snow in the winter and everything is small compared with our land – even the people are smaller. They are like you. I think you will never lose yourself in London, my son.'

His mother had taught herself English from a book and Alexis learned to read the stories she read to him, even those of Charles Dickens, whose words he found very difficult – he'd skip the hardest bits as the story usually raced and bounced along, the characters jumping off the page like jack-in-a-boxes. The last book by Dickens he and his mother read was *Great Expectations*. The book began with the boy Pip out on the marshes, contemplating the graves of his five little brothers in the churchyard, who 'gave up trying to get a living' very early in their lives. Pip came into money and travelled to London by stagecoach, where he learnt to be a gentleman. Alexis clapped his hands with delight to read about Pip's adventures.

Alone in the cowshed he dreamt of Pip rattling along in the coach and the changing of horses at stage-posts on the way. Pip and his dead siblings got muddled up with the line of dead bodies out on the plain. Alexis's dreams were untouched by grief or even horror. They were instead filled with stories and characters from stories.

When he woke it was pitch dark outside. He stood up and brushed off the straw sticking to his knickerbockers. He must get into less Russian-looking clothes. One of the servants was a Sart boy his father found abandoned in a cowshed when he was a baby. Alexander had the boy christened in the Orthodox cathedral and chose a Russian name for him – Kolya. As a servant, Kolya still dressed in Sart clothes, wearing loose dark brown trousers with a long black tunic and a blue scarf knotted round his head to keep off the flies.

Alexis walked the few hundred yards to the dacha and, taking a deep breath, headed toward the kitchen, where he found the servants lying where he'd left them. Kolya was huddled in a corner and facing the wall, like a schoolboy who had fallen asleep taking his punishment. He was bent double in a crouch to protect himself. Kolya was shot in the back. Gazing down at his friend, Alexis realised he could not use his clothes. They were soaked in blood. He pulled Kolya away from the wall, laid him on his back and closed his companion's eyes. He was taking a rest from his work. Alexis kept that thought uppermost in his mind. He was taking a rest.

Kolya kept a spare set of his clothes in a cupboard beneath the stairs and there Alexis found trousers, tunic and a blue scarf. With the scarf tied round his head he could pass for a Sart boy. He'd dirty his face a bit in the dust and adopt a more servile stance.

Alexis climbed the stairs to his father's dressing room, where he kept his money in a large silken bag the colour of emeralds. He fetched the leather money-belt sitting on one of the cherry wood tables and stuffed it with wads of thousand ruble notes from the bag, as many as he could carry. He crept downstairs slowly and out into the yard. Glancing up at a fading crescent moon, he prayed that he could find his way out of Russia.

He decided to take one of the rough tracks, which led into the new Russian suburbs of Tashkent. Alexis walked in the open with his head down, shuffling along, a tired and poor Sart boy returning from work on the land to the old part of the city, where he lived with his family in two large rooms in among the labyrinth of souks. Alexis was terrified the brigands were still close by and would recognise him. He was confident the men would have noted his special status at the head of his siblings, despite his shortness and the childlike face his parents' friends mentioned every time they paid a visit – 'The oldest child! Why, he is small – he has a baby face.'

After ten minutes or so, Alexis heard the sound of a horse's hooves and wheels. He kept walking, slowly as if he were dragging himself along, dog-tired, when the tarantass came to a halt and the Uzbek driver called out to him in his native language, 'Hey, boy, you want a lift into the city?' Alexis understood the words Kolya had taught him and shuffled forward. He nodded to the driver and stepped up into the small, low carriage which rested on two long, springy poles running the length of the carriage. When it snowed the poles served as runners, and with its wheels taken off, the tarantass became a sledge. Alexis and Kolya would hitch the family's large tarantass onto a troika and side by side they took turns at driving the sledge, lightly whipping the three horses as they trotted and cantered over the snowy plain.

The drive into Tashkent would take half an hour or longer, so Alexis lay down on the paper-thin mattress in the back of the carriage. He tried to remember the faces of his family but could only see bodies, without expression and inert. All he could think of was getting to the railway station south of Tashkent.

He remembered his father's excitement when the Central Asian Railway track arrived in the city from Samarkand in 1897. Alexis had been seven years old. 'My son, the line follows the path of the great Silk Road, where over many hundreds of years caravans and horses and donkeys, piled high with cotton, gold, silks and jewels, have travelled. When they were tired, they stopped at caravanserais along the way for food and rest and songs.' Alexis loved to hear his father talk in such a grand way and to hear him sing in his rich baritone voice – out on the farm or after supper when the family gathered round the fire for stories and songs.

The ramshackle carriage was speeding up and Alexis was being tossed about like a cork on choppy water. He could feel the poles supporting the tarantass through the thin mattress. They hurt his small body, battered his frame. I am like the boy, Jim, in *Treasure Island* he thought, slipping and sliding up and down the waves in Ben Gunn's little, lopsided coracle made of goatskins. Alexis loved that word, 'coracle'. He would roll it around his mouth, taste it on the tip of his tongue. In bed at night he chanted to himself the English words his mother had taught him that day. Cor – a – cle. Cor – a – cle. A lovely word. He touched the small gold cross he wore at all times and a sharp, razor-thin pain stabbed his heart. Then Alexis was asleep. He fell into a deep sleep, empty of dreams. In a bottomless pit lay the bodies of his family and the servants – a pit that would never perhaps yield up its horrors in all their bloody entirety.

Alexis slept on. He did not see the large trees lining the wide boulevards, the poplars, acacias and willows the Russians had planted in quadruple rows, after Major General Chernaiev and his force of nearly two thousand took Tashkent in 1865. The army had moved toward the city, strong felt wrapped around the gun wheels to deaden the noise, and with ladders they scaled the walls. With a priest brandishing his crucifix at their head, they vanquished the ancient settlement.

Alexis did not see the big houses the Russians built, with their gardens full of peach and almond trees; or the fields of cotton and sesame in between the houses and gardens where friends of Alexis's parents lived. His sleep was, though, scented with the freshness and fragrance of the cherries ripening on either side of the tarantass, as it moved into the heart of a city with a population as large as Paris, that faraway city of dreams.

He woke at dawn, sunlight filtering through a chink in the strong cotton covering the carriage. There was little sound outside and when Alexis stepped out of the tarantass, he found the driver's seat empty. He's probably gone for some chai, Alexis thought. A few yards away from the carriage was a large caravanserai, a square structure built near the railway station for weary passengers arriving in the city or for travellers fresh and eager to begin their journey. Some would travel to Bukhara to visit the bazaars and mosques – Bukhara (the 'lucky place'), the city George Curzon (a friend of Alexis's father) described as the most beautiful in Central Asia, with the people wearing all the colours of the rainbow. Bukhara, George Curzon said, was a mine of knowledge about the past. 'The city is full of wonders, Alexis. Some day you will go there.' George Curzon gave his family a book he wrote about Central Asia. What would become of that beautiful leather-bound volume on his father's walnut shelves?

Alexis entered the caravanserai through a gate which led into a courtyard open to the sky. Inside the stone walls of the square were chai stalls and niches and chambers, where travellers could sit and refresh themselves or sleep. There was a small ornamental pond at the centre of the yard, where some ducks were swimming or sunning their breasts. Alexis bought a small cup of hot black chai, into which the Kazakh vendor poured a heap of gravel sugar from China. He also bought some non bread and a cluster of red grapes. Alexis sipped the strong chai inside an empty niche. Ravenous, he devoured the non and grapes and felt his mind relax a little. He was even able to stretch out his short legs and gaze up at the blue sky and the sun above. Thank

God I am alive, he exclaimed silently. Praise be to God.

For a while Alexis lay there, too stunned to think of anything but the miracle of his being saved by God's grace. He felt elated, special. God had chosen to save him and he must prove himself worthy. His mind began to work fast. He would lay low in the caravanserai niche to avoid being identified by fellow Russians or by any of the Bolshevik railway workers, who kept a watchful eye out for Chodaks, the White Russians they despised. They might easily see through his disguise.

He knew there was a train leaving for Bukhara at midday, as his father often visited the 'lucky city' to meet with Russian colleagues in the local administration. As a diplomat, it was important for him to travel around Central Asia, making sure that the Russian authorities were treating the local population with fairness. An idealist, Alexander believed he could persuade corrupt and uncivil personnel to change their ways. Alexis listened closely to his father's ideas about Russia and its Empire. His father wished with his whole heart that Russians and Central Asians, priest and mullah, could respect each other's cultures, although he did believe in the innate superiority of the Chodaks.

Alexis pulled himself up in the niche. It was true. Father was right. Chodaks were superior and those who were chosen by God must lead the less fortunate with compassion and a clear head. Suddenly Alexis lurched forward and almost vomited as he recalled his father's blasted, gut-strewn body. He forced himself, with an iron discipline his father had instilled, to throw the bloody bits and pieces of Alexander's body into the dark recesses of his memory. He pushed the remains of his diplomat father deep down inside himself.

Exhausted by the effort this took, Alexis lay back on the cool stone. At this moment a rhythmic chanting started up, resonating all around the courtyard. Alexis raised his head, seeking the source of the chant. In a corner of the caravanserai, sitting with crossed legs on the ground, with his back resting against the wall, an old Uzbek man leant toward a little girl in a turquoise dress. Her head was misshapen and swollen. The man was touching her bowed head gently and chanting over her, a healing chant that sought to exorcise the evil spirits, the bad gods who made her head grow into such an ugly shape.

Alexis recognised the folk doctor. He was a Sart who travelled from city to city, offering his healing powers to rich and poor alike. His mother had welcomed him into their home a few years ago, when he arrived at the door with remedies the peasants and serfs had used for centuries. There was pepper brandy for cholera, fermented mare's milk to cure syphilis, the laying on of hands to relieve pain. Some of the remedies worked, especially the laying on of hands for aches and pains that seemed to have no physical cause.

Earlier in the year Tati had complained of an intense gripe in her stomach. The Russian doctor could find nothing wrong with her but when the Sart came, he spent an afternoon laying his hands on Tati's stomach and chanting over her in Uzbek. Every so often she would cry out and then he'd smile at her and go very quiet, so that he could hear the pain speaking. The next day the gripe was gone.

Alexis knew that Sarts believed music was a conduit for good and evil spirits entering and leaving the body. At the age of eight he had announced to his parents that he'd decided when he was older he would be a folk doctor.

Alexander and Catherine were surprised and pleased that Lexi should have such an ambition, but 'Lexi, you are a Russian,' his father said, 'a Chodak if you like. We enlightened Russians believe in the medicine of science, not in these old wives' tales.

'I know the Sart doctor helps some of his patients and of course Tati did recover from her pain, but that is because there was no physical reason for it. He is a good man and means well but he cannot cure real diseases. He gives poor people a great deal of comfort, but we can offer them so much more than this!'

Catherine hugged Alexis. 'My son, your father and I are very proud of you. You are a compassionate boy and to have such a dream does you great credit, but you must forget this romantic idea. When you are older, you might train to be a real doctor in the Medical Academy in Moscow. Your grandfather, Nicholas, was a very fine doctor who trained at this Academy.'

Alexis did not wish to hurt his parents so he pretended to accept their wise words, but he continued to dream of becoming a folk doctor. At every opportunity he observed the folk doctors on the streets and in the souks of Tashkent. He noted down the diseases and conditions they were asked to deal with – malaria, cholera, typhoid, epilepsy, blindness but mostly the poor people of Tashkent appealed to the holy man for relief from the rheumatics of age, head colds, sore throats and skin conditions, along with afflictions of the mind such as hearing voices, suffering from rages or simply being in low spirits, which was the most common complaint.

He watched the Sart doctor who was cradling the girl's head, rocking it gently from side to side in time with his chanting. The Sart was a charismatic who claimed that he possessed divine powers. He was a holy man descended from Sartaqtai, one of Genghis Khan's sons. The shaman's beliefs were not those of the Orthodox church, but Alexis was impressed by his mesmerising personality and the success of his practices. He hummed along with the Sart's chanting and imagined himself as a folk doctor dispensing wisdom and warding off the evil eye.

Inside the niche Alexis began to map his course. When he arrived in England he could use his knowledge of folk medicine to help England's brave people. Their climate was cold and damp, so there would be many complaining of rheumatics. They would welcome him as their little Russian saviour. When he arrived in Bukhara he'd stay with his father's Russian friends. They could loan him some money he would repay later, when his parents' substantial fortune was released from the State Bank of the Russian Empire.

Alexis had visited the magnificent bank in Moscow with his father in 1902 when he was twelve. He had wondered at the grand palatial building, which was perfectly symmetrical and had a row of newly planted trees lining the frontage.

The train to Bukhara was not due to leave for two hours so Alexis tried to get some sleep. It was a common enough sight to see people dozing inside one of the caravanserai niches and unlikely that anyone would disturb him. The second Alexis closed his eyes he heard in the pit of his stomach a muffled cry, like someone being strangled or choked. His gorge began to rise but he managed to swallow the acidic, half-digested food and chai. He sensed a bellowing, a bloodlust demanding satisfaction, a roaring for revenge against the men who had murdered his family.

Should its ugly, bitter face erupt and break through, there would be no telling what he, still a boy, might be capable of. The monster eventually grew tired and quietened, and the boy slept the sleep of the dead as if he were entombed in the stone where he lay.

****

An hour later Alexis woke with a jump to the sound of drums, flutes and trumpets, shouting and clapping. He opened his eyes to find the courtyard teeming with people. Thin patterned carpets had been spread by the walls and Uzbeks, Tartars, Sarts, even some Russians (Alexis was relieved to find no acquaintance or friend among them) were sitting, lying and standing all around the yard. At the side of the rectangular pond a group of boys, aged between twelve and sixteen or so, were dancing barefoot to the music. They wore long, brightly coloured silk smocks reaching below the knees and narrow trousers tightly fastened round their ankles. Their arms and hands sparkled with rings and bracelets and their hair was long, in some cases cascading way down their backs. The heads of the boys were shaved at the front and the nails of their hands and feet painted scarlet.

Their eyebrows were dyed jet black and painted in thick lines, which met over the bridge of their noses.

Alexis had heard of the bachas, the troupes of dancing-boys who performed in cities throughout Central Asia. He had longed to see them, but his father said he must wait till he was older as the dances were for men and not boys, and yet there were boys in the audience who were much younger than Alexis and some of them were dancing, mimicking the bachas. The mullahs did not approve of the bachas but Sarts welcomed the boys and their bazems, the passionate and sensuous dances that delighted the heart and spirit.

Kolya, his dear companion, had told Alexis all about the dancing-boys. Together they planned to run away, when they were sixteen, with a troupe passing through Tashkent. They would, of course, return after a few weeks as they did not wish to leave home for good. The bachas were nomadic and lived a splendid life, dancing in Bukhara and Samarkand and cities undreamt of by the two boys. They dreamed of being with the bachas, sleeping out under the stars and changing into costume after glittering costume at each new dance.

The flutes and trumpets were playing faster and faster, the kettle drums beating furiously, and the boys' bodies shaking and pacing and writhing to the music. Their hands and arms were raised and trembling. The boys began to sing a piercing, haunting melody to the ever-increasing tempo of the wind instruments. Alexis could recognise the Uzbek and Turkic words intermingling, blending together in the songs. The boys chanted of love and the beauty of women. The music reached a scintillating climax as they sank to the floor in exhaustion, the crowd applauding, hooting and shouting their delight. Bad spirits had been expelled from their bodies. The boys had chased them away with imaginary brooms, imitating the sweeping motion of the grandmothers, mothers and sisters they had left at home. Around the pond and all over the courtyard their tired, spent bodies lay, the boys gazing up at the blue sky above.

One of the reclining bachas was looking at Alexis. He got up and walked over to a chai stall, where he bought a large bowl of hot chai and carried it over to him. Alexis rose to take the bowl from the dancer, bowed and said *Rahmat*, the Uzbek word for thank you. As he raised his head, the bacha looked Alexis in the eye, winked and smiled before walking back to the group.

Alexis would not have missed the boys' dance for anything, but now he must leave Tashkent. England was his destiny. This was his grand plan. The idea of arriving at the 'White Cliffs' his mother had told him about, filled him with longing. The white cliffs. A clean slate he might write his name on. To belong to that great country and its Empire would be an honour. As its esteemed guest he would prove loyal and trustworthy. The new King Edward would welcome him as Russian nobility. Alexis was keen to prove his worth.

The dancers and their audience were beginning to stir from the ground. This was a good moment for him to go out and purchase a ticket for Bukhara, as the train would soon be leaving.

When the train chugged into the station, smoke steaming from the engine, ten or so people walked out of the caravanserai onto the platform. The bachas stayed inside, preparing for their performance that evening. Alexis headed for the last carriage where he found a seat on one of the benches screwed to the floor. There were six other passengers in the carriage, an Uzbek family – mother, father and four young children – who carried little apart from some small bundles, probably containing clothes and food, which were in a heap on the floor. They were listless and thankfully quiet, even the children, who were curled around their parents, half-asleep.

Maybe they were going to Samarkand, the city that shimmered (his mother said) with brilliant blues and deep turquoise domes. Alexis sighed, and as the train chugged out of the station he closed his eyes. He had travelled outside

Tashkent twice in his life, once as a baby and that memorable time when he and his father went on a very long journey by horse and carriage up to St. Petersburg and back to Tashkent via Moscow in 1902.

That journey, when he was twelve years old, had taken over four weeks and four cavalry soldiers from the Imperial Guard had accompanied father and son to protect them from bandits. To pass the time they had read aloud to each other. They had four leather-bound volumes of the great Tolstoy's *War and Peace*, which took them two weeks to read, and another four volumes of George Eliot's *Middlemarch*.

Alexis was surprised when his father told him George Eliot was a woman called Marian Evans. He had thought only men wrote books. What a fine woman this Marian Evans must have been to write such a long story, with so many twists and turns in it, and such an abundance of characters, whose lives were caught up inside a great network like the many railway lines that criss-crossed each other all over the little country of England. Tolstoy and Marian. He loved them both. Did they write to each other? Alexis wondered. Such great minds should meet often. Yes, there was much to learn from such writers.

The children in the carriage were livelier now and began to be curious about Alexis, who was keeping his eyes firmly closed, as the train passed through plain and desert land. When he felt a tap on his knee, he pretended not to notice, but then someone tapped harder with their knuckles and Alexis at last opened his eyes. A waiflike face was close to his and the dark brown eyes of a small girl were gazing at him. She spoke to him in Uzbek – 'Ismingiz nima?' Alexis knew he was being asked his name but feigned ignorance of her language. She pointed to herself, 'Mening ismim Tati.'

Nausea caught Alexis by the throat and he retched violently in his seat. The girl was startled, frightened, and ran back to her family, pointing at Alexis. Her mother held the girl close. She thought the boy (a Sart by his clothes) was either drunk, or worse, might be ill with cholera or malaria.

She told the children not to go near him and the father nodded his agreement, giving Alexis an accusing look.

Tati, Tati, Tati. The little sister he had cradled in his arms at dawn, her little body blown to bits, not a trace of her laughter and smiles left. Was he a coward to have left his family behind? Should he have at least covered their bodies, buried them in the fertile soil fed by melt-water from the mountains? Such an oasis of fruit he had picked all through the past year with Tati – peaches, almonds, apricots, grapes and nuts he didn't know the name of. They had played in the fields of wheat and cotton and sesame and rice and he had chased Tati round and round the mulberry and fig trees. She knew he could see her wherever she hid, but all the fun was in the pretending, the waiting, the wanting to be found.

Alexis felt hollow. He had stopped himself retching again by sheer willpower. He ate some non he had left from the morning and drank the remains of the chai, which the cara-vanserai vendor had poured into his leather flask. The words of Alisher Navoi, 'the Chaucer of the Turks', the poet his father revered, returned to him in snatches: 'learning is knowledge acquired in small portions, treasure the moment, it will not last; only the fool lives in future or past, a ruined land will soon be made to flower':

> He who stands apart or turns his face
> Deserves no place in the human race.
> In the midst of a crowd alone he stands;
> Even to clap requires two hands.

6

Portland Place

Central Asia, Tashkent, Bukhara, the Silk Road – Alexis's story had swept Meg away. She felt like applauding her grandfather's courage in the wake of such a tragedy. Hazel, her grandmother, was 'the true author' of this extraordinary tale. Of course. There were many authors in Hazel's family, a cousin who wrote detective fiction and a sister who was a features writer for a woman's magazine. Her father had, in later years, told Meg that Hazel had read and written a great deal in her spare time, especially after she retired from The Free at the end of the war.

How many times had her father read this manuscript Alexis had given him all those years ago? Had he read it at all? Meg wondered. Maybe he had only given it a cursory glance. The paper was fresh and unmarked. Her grandmother wrote well. You could hear Alexis's energetic voice telling her the story, gesticulating and exclaiming as he forged ahead, supplying her with every detail, every colour. The desire to escape, it seemed, had compelled Alexis to put the memories of his past behind him.

Meg was spellbound by the fairy-tale quality of his story. How far it was weighted on the side of fact or fiction, she was unlikely to discover. Her father had known nothing of Alexis's history and nor had Hazel's family. Meg had herself spent some time last year researching the history of Russians in Central Asia at the School of Slavonic Studies in London, but had come up with nothing so far. This account was all she had.

****

1938

Alexis closed his book and placed the leather-bound volume on the rosewood table beside his bed. Tonight he was reading *Middlemarch* for the third time, having recently bought a first edition in four volumes at one of the second-hand bookshops on the Charing Cross Road. Thirty-six years ago he and his father had read Marian Evan's stupendous book to pass the time on their journey to Petersburg, and now here he was in his middle age, struck afresh by the exceptional depth and warmth of Marian's writing.

Before arriving in England he was already in love with his chosen country. She had introduced him to this fine country, its green lands and the close-knit people living in villages and farms. Alexis liked the littleness of England, where a foreigner such as himself could establish himself. Here in London he was rubbing shoulders with many famous people. He himself was in the gossip columns.

Alexis sighed. His son, Vasili, who was playing Chopin on one of the pianos downstairs, seemed more foreign than he was himself. His son, with his black hair and melancholy looks, struck people as Jewish. They were surprised he was Alexis's son. He was so thin and his movements were slow, lethargic. Alexis listened to his son and sighed again. Vasili did not have a natural ear for music but he did execute the piece with tenderness.

His un-English boy seemed adrift in the world, uncomfortable. He loved classical music but could not sing or play to save his life, and his tastes were too narrow. The boy had no interest in opera or in the Russian songs his father hummed and sang in the bath. Bach, Beethoven, Chopin and Brahms. These composers were his son's passion and that was good, very good, but he should open his ears, broaden his appreciation.

It was ten o' clock one Indian summer's evening and Alexis and Hazel had gone to bed early. They would be up tomorrow at the crack of dawn for work. Later they would have a farewell dinner for Vasili, who was returning to his public school in Buckinghamshire for the final term before going up to Cambridge.

The school was a magnificent English building with its columns and state rooms, its porcelains and paintings. Alexis enjoyed walking round the beautifully laid out gardens, the pavilions and grottoes. The great Capability Brown in the eighteenth century was once the head gardener at his son's school. He was commissioned to lay out the gardens, Alexis boasted to his friends and patients.

Hazel was already asleep but Alexis was still wide awake. He settled back into the bank of three feather pillows, plumped up behind his head. He wished he had been alive to meet Marian Evans in London. She died at the age of sixty-one, far too young, but she made her mark. Beneath the dome of the British Museum Reading Room, Alexis had read about Marian's father, Robert Evans, who managed an estate in Warwickshire. He respected such origins. Her father was also a man who knew about the land and how to look after it.

One day he would buy a home in the English country-side. He had already amassed a collection of paintings by the great master, John Constable, and in a bigger house he could display them properly. Many were in storage or on loan to private galleries in London. One day he would be a true English gentleman, with a farm and a big house in the country.

His son was a metropolitan. He had grown up in Bloomsbury and Portland Place. He was not robust like himself. Vasili was not of the heroic type. He did not possess the full-blooded passion. He did not know himself yet. Maybe that was his own fault. He should have talked to the boy more, but he had always been so busy with building up his practice and making a name for himself. As a child, Vasili used to ask him about his past in Russia and he had refused to talk about it. Now his son never asked.

The faces of his dead family were still blurred. He rarely recalled their features. He could remember himself as a boy, but those around him were ciphers, shadows. The music, songs and dances he had not forgotten. They were a part of him, fresh and vital as a new-born child. But the dancers had no faces and the singers and musicians were indistinguishable from their songs.

Many years ago, when Vasili was at prep school, Alexis and Hazel sat down together to write the story of his escape from Tashkent. He told Hazel the story and she wrote it, stringing his sentences together, getting the English right, adding bits and pieces of her own, so that 'it makes sense', she said. Alexis's Russian accent was still strong and his English not good.

They had yet to show the unfinished tale to Vasili. His son knew the bare bones of the history, the murders and his father's flight, but that was all. Why did he not want his son to read this? Maybe he preferred to keep his past a secret, with only Hazel knowing the truth. No, that was not quite right. Alexis suspected that the story of his adventure was rather too active and colourful for his moody, grey boy. Let him spread his wings and make his mark, and then one day he would give the history to Vasili. For now, though, there must be work, work, work from dawn to dusk. Work hard and everything will turn out alright.

Alexis removed two of the pillows and lay back on the one remaining. He turned to look at Hazel. He loved his wife so very much. Before she drifted off to sleep, they had talked about their work that day, but mostly they spoke of Vasili and his going up to Cambridge. They agreed university should be good for him. 'He will meet more intelligent and cultured young men at Corpus Christi, I feel sure. That should be the making of him, Lexi.' Alexis was less certain about this than Hazel. He distrusted the English upper classes full-stop, but at least these young men would be reading and thinking.

Alexis gazed at the dark pink velvet curtains. The place he had reached in his life came to him, as always, as a tremendous surprise. Every night he stretched out his short limbs and took stock. With his stubby hands clasped behind his head, he felt a thrill of pleasure at being here in his own English home beside Hazel. Here he was at No. 46, Portland Place, the grandest street in Georgian London, the brain child of Robert and James Adam circa 1778. Alexis had secured this impressive berth four years ago and every night, like clockwork, he counted his blessings and the names of the places he had passed through before arriving in London.

From Tashkent to Bukhara by train and over the Caspian Sea to Baku, he had travelled as a Sart boy. Apart from buying food at stalls on station platforms or relieving himself at the side of the train at stops, he had feigned sleep and sickness all the way. If anyone approached him he retched and often the nausea was real. On the ferry to Baku he was sick as a dog. After arriving in the hugely rich oil city, he'd sought out Russian friends of his family, who supplied him with a great deal of money in various currencies, along with jewels he might sell in London. The city was bursting to the brim with banks – Swiss, British, French, Belgian, German, Swedish and American investors such as the Rothschilds had rushed for the oil in the 1870s. Alexis had loved to hear his father talk of the great 'rush'. He pictured being swept away in a crowd of jostling prospectors.

Next came the journey up through Russia by carriage, cart and train, arranging with his father's bank in Moscow for the release of the family's large fortune once he had settled in England, and then over the great Baltic Sea to Denmark and finally to London. Hurry, hurry, hurry.

Alexis saw himself, a speck in the far distance, a tiny speck holding the capacity for great things, stupendous accomplishments. There had been no time to stop and look around. A berth with a Russian family in London, an English education, medical school in Edinburgh and then back to London just before the war began in 1914. His feet had barely touched ground for ten years. He was, to his many acquaintances, a little Russian dynamo, a whirligig, a busy bee. He was very popular, creating a stir each time he entered a room. The little Russian gave the impression of being on the cusp of performing some extraordinary deed, a feat that had never before been dared in the history of the world.

The family fortune, which was not quite so large as he had expected, had been held in trust in a City bank until he was twenty-one. By the time the Great War broke out, Alexis was in full possession of the money. There was enough for him to live on comfortably without the necessity of earning an income, but his father had worked hard as a diplomat, and it never occurred to him that he should not apply himself as energetically in his chosen field. He still held his ambition to be a folk doctor and, after training in medicine (as his parents had urged him), he began looking into more unconventional treatments, closer to the practices of the Central Asian folk doctors he admired.

Alexis read Rudolf Steiner, whose ideas about the treatment of mind, spirit and body he assimilated with enthusiasm. He digested knowledge with lightning quickness and became increasingly impatient with the conservatism of the British medical establishment.

After some deliberation, Alexis decided to train in medical gymnastics, a new Swedish treatment awarded a Royal Charter in 1920. The philosophy of treating the body and the soul, the use of music and the laying on of hands as a means to healing, accorded with his principles. For adopting this practice he was struck off the Medical Register. 'They are imbeciles!' Alexis fumed, and in defiance of the authorities, he established a thriving practice in his house in Portland Place.

Here he was, in among the Georgian squares and medical establishments laid out with such mathematical precision between Regent's Park to the north and Wigmore Street to the south. Alexis knew people talked of him as a Cossack. He would not mind being mistaken for a Sart, a folk doctor, a healer, but a belligerent Cossack he was not. Returning from a concert and sherry at the Wigmore Hall or from the latest Mickey Mouse with Hazel and Vasili, Alexis cut a trim waist-coated figure with his tall, slim wife at his side. Their dark-haired boy, with the aspect of an aesthete, walked between his parents, his arms linked through theirs.

Alexis stretched out and shifted to find a more comfortable position in bed. He turned again to contemplate Hazel, who was fifty but still youthful. Her eyes were marine blue and they twinkled but refused the 'small-talking' Alexis loved, as he bobbed and weaved in among the guests at the lavish parties he and Hazel hosted on the last Saturday of every month, rain or shine.

They had met for the first time when Alexis attended one of her lectures at The London School of Medicine for Women in Bloomsbury. Men were not usually allowed into the lectures but, as Alexis was demonstrating anatomy at the school, he was made an exception. Much to the amusement of the women students, the 'little Russian' had applauded 'the lady doctor' with rapturous enthusiasm.

Hazel was four years older than Alexis and they shared a passion for flying, so their first date was at the Stag Lane airfield where they both qualified as pilots. Two years later, in 1917, they married. That was the year of the bloody revolution in Russia. Alexis thanked God he was in England.

Hazel loved to introduce 'Lexi, my Tashkenti husband' to her many London friends, some of whom were already his patients. 'I trained at the Society of Massage and Medical Gymnastics in Tavistock Square!' he would beam, when they asked about his qualifications. Yes, I am the doctor from Tashkent, Alexis mused, his hands tightly clasped over his chest. He was not feeling at all sleepy. He recalled the Sart doctor in the caravanserai who had chanted over the girl's misshapen head, the little girl in the turquoise dress. Who would believe how far he had come? What an impressive set of letters followed after the name Chodak, the Uzbek word for 'White Russian' he had adopted on his way to England: Dr. Henry Alexis Nicholas Chodak. His family's real name he told no-one, not even Hazel and Vasili. To recall it would be too painful.

Alexis loved the letters he had acquired in his new country. Handwritten neatly or scrawled in haste on slim, cream-coloured envelopes, or typed on a communication from his bank, he admired all those fellows, those characters strung out in a long row like pretty maids – MB, MRCS, LRCP, SMMG, MC, the last the Military Cross he had won in the war. He could count on all sixteen of them.

The name Chodak was very apt. When one of the new Kodak box cameras, a gift from Parisian family friends, arrived at the family dacha one morning in the 1890s, they had all been struck by the name. They were 'Chodaks'. Alexis and his family had taken lots of photographs with the camera, their little 'magic box'. When they had used up the films sent by their friends, both camera and film were returned to Paris to be developed. The photographs and the camera, with a new film installed, were then sent back to Tashkent.

Had the photographs survived? Alexis wondered. Was an Uzbek family living at the family dacha, or Bolsheviks? Had the pictures been thrown out, or burned, as Chodak rubbish? Alexis could not recall the faces in the photographs, only their shiny surface.

Suddenly a picture flashed into Alexis's mind, not in black and white as in the photographs, but in colour. There he was, a boy wearing a crimson velvet hat and indigo velvet knickerbockers. He was seated next to the blurry shape of his father in their fine landau, with the splendid troika horses all decked out in silks in their traces, the three horses in different colours – aquamarine, turquoise and gold. The Tartar driver wore a black velvet cap with peacock feathers in the brim.

They were on their way to a function at Government House. Alexis could just make out a Sart vendor in the background, offering his father and himself some bitter-sweet kvass and platefuls of dumplings. His father had thanked the Sart, but they had eaten and were not in need of refreshment. His father said orientals had an innate courtesy which we Russians would be advised to emulate.

And then Alexis and his father were standing in the smoking-room at Government House. Divans, covered in Bokharan velvet, lined the walls, which were decorated with oriental pictures in scarlet and gold. And now Alexis was standing in the middle of the large empty ball-room. His father's friend, George Curzon, said the room was big enough to hold 'the dancing population of Tashkent!'

He was twelve years old and almost a man. He was the only person in the ballroom. Alexis looked down and saw fresh blood lapping, washing over his feet. Where were his shoes? The blood was up to his knees, his thighs. The blood was thicker than water and it was coming in great waves. He was going to drown.

****

Alexis was twisting and turning in the large bed. He had slept fitfully for several hours. Hazel was up and out of the house half an hour past, off to get her bus to The Free where she worked as the senior pediatrician on the children's wards. Alexis woke with a jump and a sense that he had been in a maelstrom full of blood and screaming. He gasped to find Hazel's slim form had abandoned him, along with everything he possessed. He leapt out of bed and raced to the large window, where he stood immobile for thirty seconds.

This happened every morning. Every blessed morning he expected, like Aladdin on looking out of his window for his palace, to find absolutely nothing, a huge emptiness instead of Portland Place in all its grandeur and consequence. Behind him the large bedroom, his entire house, were bare, stripped of all the paintings and furniture, the oriental rugs and carpets he and Hazel had accumulated over the decades. Not a trace remained of the silver and all the precious objects. There were no servants and even the pianos, one each end of the drawing-room, had vanished along with the baby grand. Everything in his establishment had disappeared in a puff of smoke overnight.

Alexis stood by the window in his silk pyjamas and leather slippers. He was terrified of the blank space that would greet him when he opened the curtains. He retreated to his bed, the one item of any substance and comfort left, and there he sat on the edge, wondering what on earth to do. He wept like a child for a good five minutes (as he did every morning) and then, miracle of miracles, the treasured bits and pieces of his house fell back into place. He got up and drew the velvet curtains with a flourish, as if to say, 'Yes, I can face the day!'

He remembered the words from Omar Khayyam: 'the world is a great caravanserai with two doors: one entrance and one exit. Every day new guests come to the caravanserai.' Alexis had set these words to a Russian folk tune and at parties he sang of his past but refused to talk of it. In exile he had become an Englishman and a cosmopolitan. Doors had opened to him again and again and there were new guests, new patients arriving every day.

And yet he felt like Scheherazade must have felt when she found herself alive each morning. In his Portland Place practice he was spinning tales of well-being to his patients, hoping they would eagerly anticipate their next visit, when the story of their improving health could be continued where their doctor left off. At night he went to bed luxuriating in the wonder of it all, but would he and his patients, his 'guests', disappear?

Alexis took off his turquoise pyjamas and contemplated

his body in the cheval glass. Good. Firm muscles and not too much extra flesh. Yes, he was strong, praise be to God. One of the maids had run him a deep bath and, as he lay back in the water, he looked forward to the prospect of the day ahead of him. Mrs Marianne Stoop would arrive at 9.30 and Mrs Caroline Bliss at 11. That would give him time for a coffee between patients at 10.35. The rest of the day was full, six patients in all, and he always gave each one a full hour.

Alexis was generous in his work, relished working miracles on bodies grown snarled and crooked with arthritis and rheumatism. 'You might read my little article, 'Aspects of rheumatism with specific reference to massage', published in the journal of *The Society for Massage and Medical Gymnastics*. I may have a copy somewhere.' Alexis knew exactly where the thirty or so journals were stacked. He liked to hand a copy to a patient as if the journal were a cargo of gold. They resided beneath his large mahogany desk in a neat, diminishing pile. Sometimes he used them as a footrest.

Mrs Stoop had red hair and was big boned. Her husband was a farmer in Wiltshire and she had travelled up on the Great Western Railway, arriving promptly at his pillared doorstep. Her body was stiffening with arthritis at much too young an age. She worked long hard hours at Wood Farm, tending the animals, picking fruit and vegetables, cooking, preparing for guests. She was not a lazy English aristocrat. Alexis admired the discipline that brought her to his house each week, rain or shine. She rose early to be in time to catch the train up to London.

As he massaged Mrs Stoop's stiff, overstrained body he recalled, with an aching sadness, July 16 1918, that terrible day when the pinnacle of the Russian aristocracy, Tsar Nicholas and Alexandra and their five children, Olga, Tatiana, Marie, Anastasia and Alexis, their only son, were viciously murdered, shot by the Bolsheviks in Ipatiev House in Siberia. They even used bayonets on those who did not die instantly. His namesake, the Czarevich with haemophilia, poor child, was only fourteen years old when he died. The boy's body had not been recovered.

Alexis pulled himself up short – he must clamp down on these thoughts of Russia. He would never go back. Never. As he worked, he sang a folk song in a warm, thrilling baritone. 'We are all singers in Russia,' he'd explained to Mrs Stoop at her first consultation. 'I hope you do not mind. I like to sing the folk songs of my country as I work. This helps me treat your condition. I can feel your body's movements in my songs. The bones, they are coming alive I think.'

Mrs Stoop had grown used to Alexis singing, but at first she had been annoyed, embarrassed by it. Her Russian doctor had, though, established a very fine reputation and she had allowed his hands and voice to begin to counteract the rigor in her bones. In spite of his being a foreigner, the arthritis was beginning to be less troublesome.

'*Mens sana in corpore sano*. The great Augustus Georgii from Sweden brought the gymnastics to England. He said that the massage fine tune the senses so the body can sing.'

Mrs Caroline Bliss was very different from Mrs Stoop. A 'little *Mrs Dalloway* bird' Hazel called her. 'She flits in and out of your arms, Lexi, as if she were still a girl – fluttering and polite and so pretty and trim.' Alexis was proud to have a wife who was so well read in English literature. She had read all of Mrs Woolf's novels and *Mrs Dalloway*, her favourite, twice.

He and Hazel sometimes met the Bloomsbury people at parties or when they were out walking. Alexis had even taken a photograph with his box camera of Hazel and Mrs Woolf in Russell Square. He wished he could take a picture of Mrs Caroline Bliss as she walked into his large consulting room. She crossed the purple, green and blue patterned Berber rug that covered most of the floor, the colours faded with age.

Caroline moved quickly, her right hand holding her left shoulder. Alexis could see that she was in a great deal of pain. Her shoulder had frozen and was just beginning to get some movement back. 'It takes about two years to get the shoulder back to normal,' Alexis told Caroline. 'Today, my dear, I give you some gentle electrical and light treatment in addition to a tissue massage.' He was a little in love with Caroline. As he worked, he sang one of the Sart songs Kolya had taught him.

Alexis gazed out of the window as he massaged Caroline's shoulder and saw Vasili crossing Portland Place on his way home. He was carrying a shopping basket filled to the brim with food for this evening. He could see a French loaf and oranges. In his other hand the boy was carrying some flowers – red roses. Vasili was a very dear boy. What a blessing it was they all three enjoyed the good things in life. He heaved a sigh as he finished the song and the last touches of the massage, the tips of his fingers lingering on Caroline's shoulders.

'That is all for today, my dear. I hope this gives you some relief.'

Caroline left the house with a feeling of lightness. She had great faith in the little Russian doctor. Everyone swore by him.

Alexis, Hazel and Vasili ate together most evenings at eight. Alexis saw his last patient at five and, for another hour or so, wrote up his case notes for his patients' files. He kept his study neat and tidy and his filing system clear and uncomplicated. His many patients included lots of famous names – bankers, picture dealers, actors, dancers, writers. The names buoyed him up, as if their celebrity proved his worth. Hazel often teased him for being too easily impressed by people who had made a name for themselves. She thought he was over-keen on getting their trade. Well, of course he was. Hazel was a little unfair. She was a true blue Englishwoman and he was the doctor from Tashkent.

He knew people laughed at him behind his back, but they still came for his treatment, the society people, and they spread the word.

Alexis liked things to be shipshape and after he had made sure each item was in its place in his study and consulting room, he spent the next hour or so before dinner in and around the house. He went down to the kitchen in the basement to talk with the cook, Maisie, who was preparing borsch. Alexis had taught her over a year ago how to combine the cabbage with the beetroot, and the soup was now a regular item on their weekly menu. The servants called Alexis, Dr. Chodak, and Hazel, Dr. Hazel, as you could not have two Dr. Chodaks in the house. If Vasili went into the medical profession they would address him as Dr. Vasili.

Alexis followed the example of his diplomat father who held liberal views on the way to treat servants. 'They are not our equals, my son,' he would say, 'but they deserve our respect and we should provide them with good food and time for leisure. They must be free to live their lives outside the hours of work, my boy. If you respect them they will respect you.'

After dressing for dinner Alexis came down to the drawing-room. Having poured himself a gin and dry vermouth, he stood for a minute or two gazing out at Portland Place, where people were strolling home at dusk after a walk in the park or shopping at the market stalls in Goodge Street. He saw a couple in evening-dress get into a taxi, which would take them to the opera or a party.

Alexis lay down on the chaise longue by the window. He and Hazel had bought it the week after their marriage. They had chosen the new design in vogue and not the old rococo chaise, which was too fussy for their taste, with its cherubs and furbelows and flounces. This one, covered in dark blue velvet, had elegant clean lines and was in perfect alignment with the body.

When Hazel entered the room, Alexis got up to embrace

her. She was wearing a green silk dress with a lightly embroidered pattern of ferns. It was loose and sleeveless, perfect for an early autumn evening. When Vasili entered shortly after his mother, the three of them stood by the large hearth, Vasili between his parents. Being of medium height, the son appeared to strike a balance between his short father and tall mother. Anybody entering the room might note with surprise the strangely satisfying symmetry of the trio.

Hazel and Alexis expected Vasili to take up medicine as his profession and follow in the family line. In time he would realise that psychiatry, which he was considering, was really out of the question. To train as a psychiatrist would surely be the last resort. It was the lowest branch of medicine and chosen by those who did not cut it as real doctors. Vasili was tentative, thin and awkward in his movements. A cigarette hung from his lower lip, the ash building up. On the cusp of the ash dropping and spoiling the rug, he tapped it into the green marble ashtray on one of the small nest tables.

'How was your work today, Hazel?' Alexis asked.

This was a ritual. Every evening they talked by the hearth of how they had spent the day.

'Queen Mary visited the wards which was a colossal surprise. We were given no advance warning so she had to take us as she found us! She wore large fur cuffs on a blue silk coat and a posy of flowers in her buttonhole. She looked delightful, Lexi, and she visited every cot, one after another. She even asked me about you, Lexi. Someone has told her about your practice and she's fascinated by Swedish massage.'

Alexis nodded in appreciation. He was very glad of this royal visit.

'And what have you been doing today, Vasili?' Alexis asked.

He addressed his son with caution. He did not understand Vasili's faltering, his inability to smile with a whole heart. His sadness pervaded the whole house. Vasili's eyes narrowed. He was proud like his father. Hazel touched him gently on the shoulder. They were so very different, father and son.

'I have been playing the piano and read a little – Joseph Conrad's novella, *The Shadow-Line*. It's a marvellous book about a ship that's becalmed and a crew who are all sick. A young captain is in charge and there's a cook with a weak heart. Have either of you read Conrad?'

Vasili gave his parents a superior look as if to say, I suspect Conrad may be a little too intelligent for your tastes. I am a thinker and removed from the practical side of life. Hazel and Alexis exchanged a smile.

'No, my boy, I have not read this Polish writer, Conrad. I do not yet have the time.'

Or the inclination, Vasili thought to himself, looking away from his father toward the window. Alexis reflected that his son would surely be happier at Cambridge. He could see him sitting round his hearth with a group of friends, discussing science and medicine and this Mr Sigmund Freud his son kept talking about. This was as it should be. The passion for Mr Freud and his dangerous ideas would pass. He could picture the young men drinking mature burgundies from the college cellars. New friends and invigorating company. Alexis felt sure Vasili would find his feet.

'And you, Father, what did you do today?'

'Today was very full, my son, with patients and writing the reports. My work kept me occupied from the dawn until the dusk. Now, I think it is time that we went into dinner. Come!'

7

Ocean bed

1992

Meg stopped reading and sat for a while with the manuscript resting on her knees. Her grandfather's charisma, his
energy, his self-belief were compelling. In spite of his deep
insecurities, he had faced each day without flinching. Meg
longed to join that charmed circle of Alexis, Hazel and
Vasili. The picture of her father in the story was of a very
reserved, rather critical, young man. Nonetheless, her
father seemed to have lived an enviable life with his
parents. This wealth of detail came as a surprise to Meg.
Here was flesh on the bones of her father's very bare outline
of his past. She touched the manuscript (where was the
original? Meg wondered) half expecting it to disintegrate in
her hands after all this time.

As a small girl she had prayed each night that in the
morning she would find a fresh script outside her door. Each
day a new script would arrive, untouched and unread until
she held it in her hand. She had, over the years, held fast to
her belief that one day the longed-for manuscript would
appear. From this script, she would know what to say to
anyone who crossed her path. Of course she would have to
learn her lines, and that might be a problem, as she found
memorising anything extremely hard. Her mind jerked
away, cut off, froze and then her knee would begin shaking.

So a script had arrived. Her grandfather spoke to her. 'Come!' Alexis had commanded his wife and son and Meg too was eager to obey her grandfather's summons. Open Sesame! She did not need persuading to turn the pages of the manuscript and, wherever it led, she would follow. There were another thirty or so pages to read but Meg decided to set the story aside. She would look forward to picking it up again tomorrow or the next day. The manuscript was safe with her for now and, having put it back in the envelope, she placed it on top of the sea chest in the kitchen.

It was four o'clock and Meg made herself a cup of tea and took some flapjacks from the biscuit tin. They reminded Meg of her mother's, which melted in your mouth, syrupy and soft.

Meg sat in her armchair, mulling over the story in all its drama and hopefulness. She liked the sound of Alexis very much and appreciated Hazel, the graceful figure in the background, the 'true writer' of the story. Her grandmother's comical depiction of her husband's self-dramatisation and perpetual name-dropping, along with his warmth and generosity of spirit, reminded her of Vasili. Her father had been a great joker, making Andrew and herself laugh a lot in early childhood. She also recognised Hazel's depiction of her father as a young man – melancholy, a little supercilious and somehow at a loss.

A ship becalmed. Sadness and funny stories.

Like her father, Meg was tentative. She was absent-minded and solitary. Meg often missed her father with an intensity that would come upon her, unawares. But the story of the life she spent with him was for another day. Andrew. There was Andrew to think about – first and last. Meg was tensing up. As a small girl Meg wondered why the doctors in her family had been unable to cure her brother's epilepsy. She was still asking this question, even though she knew rationally there had been no cure. Andrew had hated doctors. He would scream at them to leave him alone. He called his father 'a shrink', 'a stupid shrink'. Meg alone understood. All those grown-up doctors and not one of them could lift a finger to save her brother. They should be ashamed of themselves.

In childhood she had sworn an oath on *The Lion, The Witch and The Wardrobe* that, if her parents died, she would stay and look after Andrew for the rest of her life. They would live at Holmwood and be very quiet, with just the two of them in the house on their own. Their food would be delivered from the village shops so they wouldn't have to go out much. They could watch television, play games, read and dance to the Beatles. If Andrew had a *grand mal*, she would call the doctor because she wouldn't know what to do.

Meg sat back in her chair. Alexis's and Hazel's manuscript was sitting on the sea chest. Their lives were over long ago. She had not known her grandparents. She and Andrew were all that mattered. The boy in Tashkent, Alexis's friend, Kolya, the dancing boys, the boy on a train going somewhere – they had all disappeared in a puff of smoke, as did the richness of her heritage. Portland Place and its magic carpets had vanished.

She would ring her friends, Robert and Elaine, ask them round for a drink, but Meg remembered they were away on their walking tour. Her neck began hurting, up to its old tricks. The degeneration in one of the vertebrae had halted in recent years, but when she got stuck or angry or depressed, the arthritis would flare up.

She was living with the dead, stepping around the bodies of those she had loved or had grown to love in their absence. On the whole, they were the peaceful dead and welcomed the presence of a woman so attached to their past. The memory of Andrew, though, was not at all peaceful. Stop, Andrew, please stop haunting me. 'I can live without you after all these years. I really can,' Meg murmured under her breath. And then she realised, in a flash, that the past was lost and gone and the person doing the haunting was no-one but herself. She banished the thought.

One after the other. Meg after Andrew. Andrew after Meg. Meg long after Andrew.

She had time for no-one else.

1965

One, two, three. The siblings counted the steps down to the Orchid Ballroom. Their feet sank into the deep pile carpet, the colour of plums. The bouncers on the door registered the forlorn looking couple but let them pass. They were keeping an eye out for the kind of boys who had beaten up Andrew at secondary school the previous year.

At the age of fourteen, Andrew had insisted to his parents that he wanted to go to an ordinary school. After two years at a special school in Sussex, Andrew returned home. The teachers and his parents were pleased with his progress and felt he would be able to continue his education at a local special school. Vasili and Jane had been very taken aback. They had tried to persuade him that the secondary school might not suit him. There would be so much school work to catch up on. Privately they feared he would be rejected by the other boys at the tough school near Epsom Downs. But Andrew had been determined and took the bus to school one fine spring morning, with his medicine to hand, along with exercise books and pens in his new brown satchel.

In the third week twenty or more boys circled the newcomer in one of the playing fields. They began to move in on him, chanting, 'Spastic! Epilleptic! Idiot! Cunt!' and then they had kicked him with their heavy boots, harder and harder, as Andrew curled up in a ball to ward off the blows. Later, Meg had listened outside her parents' bedroom door, whilst Jane comforted Andrew. Her brother was sobbing. He hardly ever cried. Jane later told Meg what had happened but she never saw the bruises.

Tonight, the bouncers at the ballroom were looking out for troublemakers, those boys who would not be satisfied if there wasn't at least one good kicking after a Saturday afternoon session at the Orchid. Andrew and Meg were barely worth a second glance. They flexed their muscles and pitied the weak.

The siblings stood facing the ballroom floor. Meg was drifting on an ocean bed. She was in deep waters and the huge, dimly lit ballroom twinkled in her eyes. At the edges and all around the floor there were bars and stools, where boys with close cropped hair drank coke and girls, with fringes in their eyes, sipped lemonade. Couples in alcoves kissed and fumbled and sighed.

Meg was a fish who could change colour, blend into the landscape. She could camouflage herself, mimic the movements of those around her. Her brother did not dream of disguising himself. That was why he was beaten up a year ago and never went to school again. She wondered what Andrew was thinking, standing there beside her.

Jane and Vasili did not like Andrew and Meg going to the ballroom, but Vasili's work was all consuming and Jane was unable to say no. Andrew and Meg said they enjoyed 'going up the Orchid' and the session '*was* in the afternoon.' The siblings were under strict instructions to return on the half past four train.

Meg pushed open the heavy door of the Ladies' cloakroom, as if she were on the cusp of a cave full of treasure. She found the room teeming with girls who looked like women. They shimmered in silks and velvets and cashmeres. They wore mini-skirts in corduroy and tight linen trousers. The colours dazzled Meg. The textures, scents and powders the girls were busy applying, created a seductive and sensuous aura. Bodies swirled in front of mirrors. Pretty eyes and back-combed hair in every possible shade, legs painted with fake golden tans, legs so much longer than hers, faces that were pouting and bold – all this swam before her eyes as she entered.

Meg was wearing a sparkling pink kilt, with a sleeveless silver polo-neck, silver pumps and twinkling gold powder she'd dabbed on her face on top of a thick coat of beige pan-stick foundation. White-pink lipstick finished the picture. Her eyelashes were caked with dark blue mascara. Meg had her own style, but it was spoiled by her dark straight hair, which was long and lank and deadened by split ends.

The visual splendor of the cloakroom was magnified by the large mirrors that lined the walls and were fixed to the ceiling. If you tired of dancing, you could lie back on one of the large seats and gaze up at yourself. At thirteen, Meg was much too shy and self-conscious to do this, but believed she would at some stage pluck up the courage.

Some girls spent over an hour in the cloakroom putting on their make-up, altering a dress, commenting on whether their friend's outfit was 'with it', 'fabulous', 'fantastic', 'smart' enough. The girls, ranging from thirteen to sixteen, arrived in pairs. Some had boyfriends they would meet on the dance floor. They talked of blokes, snogging, going all the way, having it, along with which bloke's breath smelled, which one had acne, who was a drip or a nutter.

Meg was in awe of these girls, these women who were so clear about things. They knew what they wanted and had complicated strategies as to how to go about 'getting off' with a boy. Meg worried about their words which sounded angry, laden with something cruel. She watched and listened. They seemed more definite, more real than the friends she had at school.

Andrew was in the smaller and more basic men's cloak-room for a much shorter time. He hardly registered the other boys and, having stopped for a moment to comb his short hair, he walked out into the ballroom and scanned the floor to see if he could spot Meg. When she emerged Meg saw Andrew at the edge of a circle of boys who, having straightened their ties and combed through their crops, were out on the dance floor waiting for the 'birds'.

The Epsom boys had formed a large circle. Andrew knew
some of them from a youth club near the Downs, which he
went to once in a while. No girls were allowed into the
circle. The boys were dancing to The Four Tops, the
American group who would appear on stage at three and
play for half an hour. Every Saturday there were two bands
or solo artists with backing groups, who played one after
the other for an hour – The Who, Jimi Hendrix, The Small
Faces, The Supremes, Ike & Tina Turner, the Walker
Brothers, Aretha Franklin.

There were twenty-six Epsom Mods in the circle. The
brusque and well-muscled young men looked closer to
eighteen than fifteen or sixteen, which were their actual
ages. They were nodding and bobbing to each other, as if
enacting an initiation ceremony. Every so often someone
stepped out of the circle into the middle of the dancers, to
perform a star turn, an exaggeration of the short, neat
movements of the dancers around him.

Meg watched the boys bending their arms at right angles,
moving them up and down to the beat of the music. Their
knees bent in time with their arms and they swayed their
hips slightly, occasionally twirling around, like it was not
difficult at all and could not have been hard to learn.

The faces of the Epsom boys were fixed and serious, a
dull glint of boredom in their eyes announcing to the world,
'Really I have much better things to do with my time, but
as I'm here I don't mind going through the motions in my
pressed denim jacket and Levis.' No-one smiled.

You might think that their lives depended on this dance,
getting the rhythm and turns absolutely correct, in step
with one another. They would see it through to the bitter
end. The dancer in the middle did smile. He could play the
fool a little in this dance to the death. 'I'll be there just to
love and comfort you-ou...and when all your hope is
gone...when your life is filled with such confusion and
happiness is just an illusion, darlin' reach out, reach
out...I'll be there.'

Gavin, a boy from the youth club, who visited 'Andy' at Holmwood, was at the centre of the circle. Meg found Gavin the kindest of Andrew's friends from the club. He had blonde hair and a cheerful face. He was shy if she walked into the breakfast room when he was there on his own. Being tall for his age made him self-conscious and he danced awkwardly, throwing his arms about in the air, without rhythm or a sense of containment. Gavin didn't match up and Kevin, the leader, shouted at him to 'stop mucking about and fuck off out of it! Let someone else in, you cunt!'

Meg stood beside Andrew. She liked watching the boys. She could dance as well as them but her brother couldn't dance to save his life. Andrew moved toward the dance floor. Meg couldn't bear it. No, she would not be seen with him. She walked away and around to the other side of the floor. There she placed her small leather handbag at her feet and began to dance, mirroring the movements of the boys.

There were several girls in pairs, dancing at the edge of the large circle. Meg closed her eyes and the music of The Supremes coursed through her slight body. 'You can't hurry love, you just have to wait, love don't come easy-er, it's a game of give and take, how long must I wait, how much more can I take...?' On and on Meg danced. She loved Tamla Motown almost as much as The Beatles.

Meg glanced over at the young men. They were like mechanical, wound-up toys. Why should she fear them? She could dance better than them. It was as easy as walking on her hands two hundred, three hundred times around the garden, but where was Andrew? Where was Alexis?

Suddenly Meg felt very panicky. She could not see her brother anywhere. He was difficult to make out as he was wearing an all black outfit – black cotton shirt, a thin black woollen tie and black denims. The floor was filling up, boys and girls surging in a mass towards the stage. The Four Tops and then The Supremes were about to play. The circles of boys, Epsom boys, Croydon boys, Purley boys, had broken up. There was to be no more dancing, just a crush and a struggle of bodies to get to the front. Meg still couldn't see Andrew and, without realising how she'd travelled the floor, The Four Tops were there in front of her, dressed in white and stepping out in the dance the boys had copied.

Meg arrived close beside the stage, so when the four men turned together in one synchronised movement, she could see them face on. One of the group even smiled at her. They were not like the boys in circles at all. They were black Americans, their well-muscled bodies lit by the green, red, yellow and blue lights behind them. The lights would every so often go out for a split second and all Meg could see was the dazzling white of the men's suits, as they twirled in perfect harmony with each other. These men smiled with joy. They were lighter than air. Musicians stood behind them, shadowy and vague, guitars, drums and keyboards barely glimpsed. 'Your world around is tumblin' and gone, darling reach out, reach out...'

Meg spotted Andrew at the other side of the stage in a similar position to hers. She thought he was dancing but realised he was having a series of *petit mals*, as they followed one another in quick, rhythmic succession, his arms flying out and hitting those standing near him. Andrew's whole body was caught up in the hard, regular jolting of his strong frame. Some of the Epsom boys were standing close by. One of them had been hit by Andrew. They were staring hard at her brother as Kevin pushed through them, shouting 'Fuck off, idiot! Fuck off out of it, epileptic cunt, fuck off out of here, you looney!'

Meg walked behind the stage set and over to the side where Andrew stood. The *petit mals* were over and he was telling Kevin, 'I'm staying here, mate!' The tall, angular boy couldn't be bothered to argue the case. Head-kicking came after the dance session, as naturally as dusk fell on the pavement. 'I don't give a toss, weirdo! I'll see to you later!' were his parting words, as he turned away.

Andrew was close to tears, but Meg knew he would push

her away if she said anything, so she pretended she hadn't seen. 'I'm getting the train home. I'm too tired to stay,' she said and Andrew nodded uncomfortably.

Gavin appeared at the siblings' side. 'What's going on, mate? Had another of them fits, have you? Want me to take you home?' Meg knew from the irritated but mildly compassionate expression on Gavin's fleshy face, that he didn't want his offer accepted. 'We'll be fine,' she said.

They took the train back to the village, Andrew having *petit mals* most of the way. Meg was silent. She had missed The Supremes and she might never have another chance of seeing them. She wondered what they were singing up there on the stage at that very moment – 'Where Did Our Love Go?', 'Stop! In The Name Of Love', 'Baby Love', 'You Can't Hurry Love'? Her friend Susie had seen The Supremes play live in New York on a Caravan of Stars tour. Her parents were American writers, who had decided to live in England because they liked the country. Meg didn't think she liked England much at all. She wished she was in Russia on a sledge drawn by horses through the snow. She would travel to Tashkent. Was there snow in that part of Russia?

A caravan of stars. Alexis running from Tashkent. Her headmistress at school (who was nearly eighty, had close cropped hair and skied in the Alps every Christmas) told Meg one lunchtime that there were places with courtyards in Eastern Russia called *caravanserai*, where nomads stopped to take food and drink and rest before continuing their journey. Meg thought she would like very much to be a nomad, but not an English one. She didn't like the pokey caravans English people took on their holidays. She was invited to Devon once by a school friend and her family. They took their caravan and Meg found it stuffy and ugly. The van stank of stale cheese. She preferred the sound of a caravanserai or a caravan of stars. She pictured courtyards with high walls, filled to the brim with stars dropped down from the sky and a full moon above. An Aladdin's cave resplendent and sparkling with treasure. Alexis. Alexis. Alexis. The sound of a sleigh in soft snow. A whisper. A kiss.

The Saturday after The Four Tops played the Orchid Meg arrived early on her own. Andrew said he was giving the session a miss and Meg told Jane she was going with a friend. As she walked around the ballroom, Jimi Hendrix passed her on his way to the dressing-room behind the stage. She gazed at his sad, creased face, which was like an old parchment kept inside a safe for centuries, or in a musty cave. She noticed how thin and ill he looked.

Meg kept going to the Orchid – but not every Saturday as her parents would find out soon enough she was lying about going with a friend. She was losing touch with her friends and grew more silent, closed in. She was like a conch shell on the ocean floor, folded in on herself. If you held the shell to your ear you might hear the high seas.

The life she spent with her family and at school began to fall into the background. A distance grew between the more ordinary Meg and the girl who lived in darkness. In the school holidays she liked to take the green double-decker bus into Epsom, where she sat in the cinema. She was meeting a friend.

With half-closed eyes Meg watched the films that flickered across the screen. She touched the maroon velvet seats and smoked the carton of ten she'd bought from the slot machine in the village before catching the bus. Beneath the seats there was mustiness and cigarette butts, silver paper from choc-ices, the dark chocolate coating thin as her dreams.

Meg noticed the mental patients at the cinema. They sat in the front of the stalls (she chose the middle) like they could not get close enough to the screen. They laughed in the wrong places and would shout or scream out all of a sudden. The patients were from the five hospitals in the Epsom area, including her father's. A cluster of madmen, Meg reflected. Her father was now the senior consultant at a huge hospital, where there were over a thousand patients.

Gazing at the patients in front of her, she wondered if they had ever been in a padded cell. In the past year she had stopped boasting to her friends that her father had all the padded cells taken out of his hospital. No-one was impressed. They kept on tapping their heads with their fingers. She could not get the cells out of her mind. She longed to be inside one and a million miles away from such a place. In her bedroom Meg threw herself down on the cushions scattered on her divan and imagined she was bouncing off the walls of a cell. She kept trying to have a *petit mal*. She hated her father's patients.

Once, when she was waiting while her mother collected her father from the hospital, ten 'Red Indians' in full feathered headdresses surrounded the car. She and Andrew played cowboys and Indians and she was always the Indian. There was no animosity in their eyes. They did not frighten her. She was in a nomad tent. She was one of them. Alexis was there. He was a little Red Indian and wore a headdress of red and purple feathers. The Indians did not stay long. They disappeared.

One of her father's patients believed she was an ice-cube that never melted. Vasili's stories were funny when he told them round the drawing-room fire, but when Meg was sitting by the hospital gates and close to the patients in question, they weren't funny at all. Vasili never gave their names. One patient poured a jug of iced water over his head and another announced she was a fried egg sizzling in a pan. 'Would you like to eat me, doctor?' she'd asked. The patients' stories were very hot or very cold. Was there nothing in between?

Did her father's patients feel homesick for their padded cells? Did Andrew miss the padded helmet he wore as a child? He didn't wear it anymore, as he had *petit mals* all the time and he didn't fall. At the hospital there were much more terrible things than a padded cell, like people being given gigantic electric shocks. Vasili refused to explain the shocks to Meg when she asked. Why did he let them happen? She heard of the shocks when she was eavesdropping on one of her parents' conversations. Andrew's fits were like he was having lots of shocks. How on earth could a shock be good for you?

Meg shook when he did, she felt every jerk of his muscles in her body, she became rigid with waiting for the *petit mals* to pass. The seconds the fits took seemed like eternities. She waited and waited and waited and waited in the silence.

This was not the silence Meg had craved in her dreams. This silence had to be broken. Silence for Andrew and for herself could never be peaceful. At the Orchid Meg left her family behind. There she could immerse herself in the sounds of the deep oceans. There she could be out of her depth.

After Andrew's short spell at the 'normal' school, and having turned sixteen in 1966, he began to look for work. He got odd jobs – gardening, clearing rubbish, helping out in a greengrocer's shop. For one whole spring he worked in a bottle garden factory, where he squeezed little plants into bottles of all shapes and sizes. Andrew was careful and methodical. He excelled in the work, but one day a colossal *grand mal* sent him crashing down into the bottles and his employer had to let him go. The insurance wouldn't cover it.

When Jane told Meg what had happened, the White Rabbit flashed into her mind. In *Alice in Wonderland* the rabbit falls down smash into the cucumber frames when Alice, her whole body filling his house, swipes him with her hand. She preferred imagining the rabbit in the story than her brother's pain and humiliation. Her knee began shaking. She couldn't bear how hurt Andrew was. She couldn't bear it.

Every time Andrew got a job this happened. At the beginning, he'd return in the evening, with light in his eyes and a spring in his step, but then he'd have a fit and was yet again, in Andrew's words, out on his elbow looking for another job. After a while he gave up working and became very angry. By the age of seventeen he had grown a long bushy beard and was even taller. If someone rang the front door bell and Andrew was nearby, he would charge to the door, open it with a clatter and stand there, his legs wide apart, with a belligerent expression on his face, his lips pressed together hard. He would stare at whoever was at the door for a few seconds, as if daring them to hold their ground.

'Yes, what do you want? Speak your business. What are you doing here?'

Meg would watch her brother at a distance, wondering what would happen next. Andrew didn't ever actually hit people but he could look murderous, and so could she. She mimicked Andrew and soon she wasn't sure where she began and Andrew ended, or was it the other way round? Meg followed Andrew from room to room.

She was fifteen but she couldn't recall many details of how she spent her time from day to day, from year to year. She never kept a diary, only wrote instructions to herself on scraps of paper: get up, brush teeth etc. Maybe this was normal. She did all the usual things, went to school, scraped exams, talked and ate and slept, but she didn't remember the details. Meg began to put on weight. She dreamt of lying forever on a bed with a conveyor belt running alongside her. She would reach out for the Mars Bars, Flakes and Dairy Milk chocolate bars that passed by her, an endless supply.

Meg tried to read more, newspapers and novels, but could not concentrate. It was all she could do to keep up with her reading for school. All she could think about was chocolate, toast and trifles and gorging on whole roast chickens. She gave up the idea of the script arriving at her door, setting out her conversations for the day. She longed instead for someone to arrive with a huge book and lots of ideas. This person, a man, would tell her what to do, how to forget the chocolate and shed the two stones she had gained so rapidly.

When there was a race meeting, gypsies came with the fair that filled one side of the Downs. One summer, when she was sixteen, Meg went into a caravan to have her fortune told by an old woman with a red headscarf and gold hoop earrings. She gave half a crown to the gypsy, who studied the palm of Meg's left hand. 'There are lots of beginnings,' she said, 'the lines keep fading out and then they start up again somewhere else. You will begin over and over and over again, my dear, and this will be very tiring for you, but one sunny day when you are older, you will stay on a path and arrive somewhere.' The old woman, whose face was wrinkled and brown and weather-beaten, smiled at Meg, who wished she could stay in the caravan forever.

****

Meg opened her eyes. She had dropped off to sleep in her chair and woke to find her neck hurting. She stretched and stood up to look out at the common. Meg felt depleted and helpless in the presence of these disturbing, fitful memories. She longed to see Robert and Elaine, and their little boy, Dom, who had recently celebrated his fifth birthday. Sometimes her friends dropped Dom round to spend time with her on his own. He felt very grown up then (as did Meg) when they kissed him and left, 'Bye, bye, Dom – see you later, have a lovely time with Meg!'

Meg missed her friends, who would be travelling back from Scotland by now, she reminded herself. Her mood lifted slightly. She looked at her watch. Eight pm. She would take a deep bath and cook some dinner. After that there might be time to read the last chapter of Alexis's story.

The small bathroom was off the hallway hub. Meg turned on the hot tap and added some pine bath essence her mother had given her when she came up from Somerset for the day earlier in the year. She lit some candles and turned off the light before laying back in the bath. Closing her eyes, she could feel her mind relax and her body become less tense. Half an hour later she prepared some pasta, which she ate quickly and then sat down in the armchair to continue reading.

8

Chain Pier

1948

Alexis peered through the window's lattice pattern of diamonds, gazing out at the tall elegant lady and the thin young man with such a sad face at her side. Here were his dear wife and son. That he was married to an English woman and had established himself in the English country-side, often came as a surprise to Alexis. Sitting in the caravan he would sometimes recall Tashkent and the rich scents of the souks. He studied Hazel and Vasili as they walked toward the caravan which stood in a wilderness of long grass and wild flowers. Suddenly he broke out in a broad smile and jumped up from his desk, waving and blowing kisses as they walked past. His wife and son had been in the small topiary maze. They were on their way into the dining-room for breakfast.

Alexis and Hazel first viewed The Grange at the end of 1938, just before the war. They had fallen in love with the large country house in Huntingdonshire and, in their tour of the grounds, they had come upon the little maze and the elephants, birds and squirrels carved in its yew hedges. You could barely distinguish the animals and birds from the hedges, they were so overgrown. 'They need a good trim,' the agent had apologised, but Hazel had protested, 'The maze is perfect as it is – you see the little animals emerge just as you are trying to make out the shape – it's delightful!'

It was a mild Sunday morning in April and Alexis had been up since seven, so that he could work in the caravan for a couple of hours before breakfast. Maisie, the cook, had made him some strong coffee in a large cup and brought it out on a tray with a bowl of brown sugar. Alexis ground the coffee beans himself at weekends, so there was always a large tin packed with fresh grains for the week ahead. Alexis stirred four heaped teaspoons of sugar into his coffee.

Before the war Alexis had decided to take up farming whilst keeping up his practice in London. The Grange and its farm were the first property he and Hazel viewed and they had come upon the caravan in the garden, after the agent had left them to walk around on their own. When they first saw the caravan they thought it was a tiny house, as the roof was tiled, but on closer inspection you could see the wheels. The hinges of the door were rusted, but Alexis had pushed it open easily with a gentle shove of his shoulder.

Inside they had found two fitted gas lamps, a rickety old table and chair, and a bookshelf holding some very old volumes of poetry. The books were damp and yellowed with age, but Alexis later took them into the house to dry them out and placed the volumes on one of the empty shelves in the small, wood-panelled library, as if he already owned The Grange. 'This library, it waits to be filled!' he had exclaimed.

Hazel would tell friends that it was the topiary maze and the caravan that persuaded them to buy. The elderly agent showing them round did not know the caravan's history but thought it must have belonged to the first owner, an architect who built The Grange at the turn of the century and lived there himself. 'He was a follower of William Morris and keen on the idea of 'the simple life' – hence this caravan, I should think.' After they had moved in, Alexis had installed electric lights and put up two new shelves as the old ones were rotten. He threw out the damp and mouldy table and chair and installed a modern kneehole desk and a pine upright chair. In St. Ives, the nearest town, he bought a small one bar electric fire to heat the caravan in winter. Hazel instructed the gardeners to keep the grass long in the caravan's vicinity.

Every morning before breakfast and in the evenings before dinner, Alexis sat for an hour or two in the caravan, his knees fitting neatly under the desk with room to spare. There he settled his accounts, drafted letters, drew up plans for the farm. In any time there was left, he'd read George Eliot or Tolstoy. The much thumbed leather-bound editions of the authors' novels filled one of the shelves. Alexis kept his files of business papers on the other. In the winter, or during prolonged spells of rain, Alexis would carry the books and papers into his study, which was next to his dressing room upstairs.

In a stroll round the garden, Hazel liked to come upon her husband in the caravan, bent over his papers or reading. He looked like a fortune teller, but when he raised his head and smiled at her through the window, he was Alexis again, her little Russian spouse.

Alexis was very snug. He was reminded of the horse-drawn tarantass which carried him into Tashkent on that fateful day over forty years ago. He recalled the bachas, the dancing boys, and thought of Kolya crouched in the kitchen, shot in his back. The past would return to him as a sudden vignette. Kolya above all he recollected, with his dear face turned to the wall. He had straightened his body and laid his friend on his back, gazing into his deep brown eyes before gently closing them for ever. Outside the inert and disorderly line of bodies reproached him for his neglect.

The wheels of the caravan had rusted long ago, making it a permanent fixture on the estate. Inside this small house he was safe. He thanked God he was alive.

Alexis had never regretted buying The Grange and he had quickly established himself as a breeder of pedigree Ayrshire cattle. Farming was in his blood. His Tashkent

The Sound of Turquoise

family had owned swathes of land. The farm workers came from as far as the Scottish Highlands, eager to work for the Russian farmer who respected their work and was prepared to pay well over the odds for their specialist knowledge. They were impressed by the hours Alexis put in. The little Russian was not afraid of hard work. On Fridays he saw his patients up in London and for the rest of the week he was out and about the farm or canvassing for business far and wide.

Alexis finished his work in the caravan and took a walk around the garden before going in to breakfast. He did this every morning, to remind himself of how far he had travelled and of the property he had acquired. The Grange was a generous house, well proportioned and comfortable. Standing at the top of the garden, he gazed at the two tiers of lawn, which were perfect rectangles. The upper lawn sloped down to a bank with some stone steps in the middle. These led to the flat lower tier and a small rectangular pond overgrown with ferns and rushes. Several cane chairs were placed a few feet from the edge.

After a long breakfast over the newspapers, the family went their separate ways. Alexis was to see his overseer about the sale of one of his Ayrshires and Hazel, retired now for two years, would read and write in her study. Vasili was to pack, as he was returning to London the next day, prior to beginning work as a psychiatrist in a Surrey hospital. He had qualified in medicine and psychiatry with flying colours and was looking forward to immersing himself in his first responsible position. He was still on the thin side but was beginning to gain some weight and had grown strong from regular hiking and climbing in the Lake District with friends.

Benjamin Britten was to join the family for dinner in the evening. He had met Hazel and Alexis over eight years ago at a concert in London and asked them if they would like to be involved in preparations for the first Aldeburgh Festival in 1948. Since then they had met on several occasions and had become firm friends. Alexis was to exhibit some of his Constables at the festival and this evening he and Britten would discuss which pictures from his large collection would be included.

A little before eight Alexis was standing by the oak cocktail cabinet in the drawing-room, dispensing drinks. He was wearing his dark green velvet smoking jacket and his young friend was dressed informally in thin flannel trousers and a navy V-neck sweater.

Whilst Alexis poured the drinks, Vasili was playing a Chopin prelude and later he would play some Schubert or Scriabin, or one of the Russian folk tunes his father had taught him.

Hazel had joined Britten by the hearth. Her dark hair, now streaked with grey, was up in a roll. She wore a dove grey silk suit and the pearl necklace Alexis had bought her last year. Alexis had poured them all some chilled hock in misty green glasses with long stems. They began to talk about the many small drawings by Constable, Gainsborough and Thomas Girtin on the walls of the drawing-room. Britten was asking Alexis about a tiny Gainsborough, a shepherd boy beside a ruined hut.

'This is of a landscape near Kingston in Surrey, Benjamin – not far from where Vasili begins his work as a doctor. It is very delicate and precise, I think?'

'Yes, it's lovely. What a wonderful collection you have here.'

'Yes,' Alexis smiled, 'I have nearly one hundred paintings and drawings. Strangers ring and they ask if they can visit The Grange to see the art on my walls. I show them around, but I go with them in case of, how do you say, slippery fingers! Most of the works are by the Master, Constable, and I also have drawings by Turner and four in oils by Mr Walter Sickert. One is of the pretty French harbour, Dieppe. I met Mr Sickert at a London party. He was a cosmopolitan, you know. He sadly died not long ago.'

Britten smiled.

'Benjamin,' Alexis continued, barely drawing breath, 'I have a surprise, but it will wait until after dinner. I will show you then. Come – food awaits us!'

Alexis ushered them all into the dining-room, where the table was laid with silver cutlery and white linen napkins in silver rings. There was a large pottery bowl in the middle of the table, filled with water and rose petals, red, white, pink and apricot, floating on top. Beside the bowl there was a wooden platter of fruit – apples, oranges, bananas and black grapes. Two tall green candles were lit and stood at each end of the round mahogany table. The colours of the fruits lapped each other in the candlelight and shadows.

Before they sat down Alexis turned on the lights so that his guests could look at the many small watercolours by Constable on the walls – sketches of Suffolk churches, cattle, old mill houses, fishing villages, skies and clouds. 'The Master understood perfectly the Suffolk landscape.' Then he added, smiling, 'He liked to play a flute, like Orpheus.'

Britten was delighted with the pictures and for most of the meal he, Alexis and Hazel talked of art and music and literature. They ate chicken in white sauce, and for pudding fresh pears simmered in red wine and cloves, accompanied by dollops of clotted cream from a local dairy. There was a generous cheeseboard and the fruit, then coffee and brandy or liqueurs. Vasili was silent, nodding occasionally in agreement with what someone was saying, but mostly he concentrated on his food. When they had finished Alexis turned to his friend.

'And now, Benjamin, I show you the *pièce de resistance*, a big surprise for you! Come!'

They all got up from the table and followed Alexis into a large room, which had once been used as a billiards room, but was now a picture gallery. There was a small, light blue curtain drawn over a large painting above the hearth. This was Alexis's latest acquisition and even Vasili had yet to see it. The four of them stood in a semi-circle, gazing up at a tempestuous scene which Alexis began to describe.

'Here is one of Constable's great six-footers. I bought it at Agnew's a month ago. Such a stormy scene! It is called *The Marine Parade and Old Chain Pier, Brighton*. The Master painted it in 1827 when his wife, Maria, she was suffering from the tuberculosis. They travelled to Brighton for the sea air. The great man, he did not like the resort, he thinks it is the Piccadilly-by-the-sea. No-one bought the picture in his lifetime. The critics they thought it was too fierce for Constable, not so gentle as the pictures of farms and ponds. But I say to them, "What of his skies?!"'

'Here we have the sea-shore. There is a storm coming. The fishing boats, they are falling over in the breeze, trying to find their way to the shore. At the edge of the water the men and boys are pulling the nets in and see, here are two women walking close to the waves. One of them holds an umbrella. She thinks she is at Kew Gardens in a light shower. Such a woman as this, she is not afraid of the waves crashing so close to the hem of her skirt.'

Britten was studying the painting closely. He asked Alexis about the slim figure, the man standing with a telescope at the waterside.

'He attracted my eye before anything else. Somehow he stands at the heart of the picture but I'm not sure of the significance. Why is he not using the telescope, do you think, Dr. Chodak?'

'I am not sure, Ben. My eye did not light on that figure. I first look at the green-blue sea and the sunlight coming through the dark clouds. Then I see the boat on the left high and dry, and the man with the red hat sitting on a barrel. The touch of red is in the ladies' shawls. That is Constable's trading mark, the little bits of red.'

'I wonder why Constable called it *The Marine Parade and Old Chain Pier* when the parade and the pier are so distant. The pier looks flimsy. I find it a rather uncomfortable painting, Lexi – so different from the others we have.'

'Do you plan to exhibit this?' Britten asked Alexis. 'I have

Carlos's Note for the exhibition. *Chain Pier* would of course take centre stage.'

'No, Benjamin, I don't think I will exhibit this one. It will not suit. The pictures I exhibit at Aldeburgh are many times smaller, little gems. This grand painting will, how do you say, over-dwarf them. This magnificent picture I leave at home.'

Over coffee Alexis and Britten talked of Aldeburgh whilst Hazel and Vasili discussed his plans for the next day. She and Alexis were still doubtful about their son's choice of psychiatry as his speciality, but they accepted Vasili's choice. He himself was excited by the prospect. 'Psychoanalysis is the coming thing, Mother and Father, it really is!'

Britten was showing Alexis the draft Programme Book for the festival.

'I wanted you to see the note Carlos drafted for your exhibition. He will need a list of the paintings you plan to exhibit.'

Alexis began reading aloud, "His was one of those minds which achieve greatness in art not by straining at horizons." Yes, Ben, this is good, very good. A mind not straining at horizons. Yes. "His was the farmer's eye that can take in at a glance all the signs and portents of the land. It is perhaps significant,"' and at this point Alexis's face glowed with delight, "It is perhaps significant that Dr. Chodak, the owner of this fine collection of Constable pictures, is himself a farmer whose work in the breeding of Ayrshire cattle has won him international fame." Benjamin, please you will thank Peacock. That is so good of him to write.'

****

1992

The story came to an abrupt halt. Meg fetched the brown envelope to see if there were any more sheets of paper inside and found none. The account was unfinished. She felt cheated. The world of Alexis and Hazel was so enchanting, so full of culture and purpose. And then suddenly there was nothing. Meg was angry at her grandparents for this sudden curtailment, for not following the story to its conclusion.

Meg got up and took a pencil and notebook from her desk in the bay and jotted down some of the dates mentioned in the story. Her father had met her mother in London later that year, 1948. They had fallen in love and married in the July of 1949. In that same year, after the second Aldeburgh Festival, Alexis and Hazel's lives had fallen apart in a catastrophic chain of events. This was the climax of her grandparents' drama which Meg had known all along, the denouement she could recite by heart since Jane told her at the age of ten, eleven perhaps. She had become so immersed in the flow of Hazel's absorbing story, she had forgotten the ending. The conclusion was all she had ever known before reading this manuscript.

Appreciating the texture of life at The Grange, Meg was startled and then sad to think of how much had been lost. She noted that her father was a very thin presence in the story, but then so was Hazel. The 'real writer' had kept herself and her son in the wings, standing aside to usher in the main act, Alexis, who was about to abandon the stage. He had let them all down, when everything appeared to be going so well. Meg imagined Hazel making notes on Britten's visit in her study later on that evening. She studied the manuscript. Of course, this was the carbon copy Hazel had left for Alexis, in spite of what happened. She had wished to remind him of the time they had enjoyed, the story they had written together. He had held on to the manuscript.

It was two am and Meg knew she was up for the night.

She was tired, but the idea of bed at this moment was out of the question. She poured herself some more wine in one of her green glasses with the long stems. Settling back in her armchair, a picture came into her mind. For a while she just sat there, her eyes closed. Meg was taking in every detail, and then she got up and sat down at her desk. She would finish Alexis's story for him. Meg wrote for nearly three hours and by the time she had finished, she could hear the milkman's lorry outside and the clanking of crates as he made his deliveries.

****

I was at The Grange, my grandparents' house, and gazing up at a large square space above a fireplace. All I could see was the dusty outline of a frame and a huge patch of dirty white. I was on my own and a bitterly cold wind was blowing through the picture gallery. Doors were banging all over the house and I could hear owls hooting in the darkness outside. I walked into every room downstairs and then into the bedrooms, bathrooms, dressing rooms and studies upstairs. Only a few pieces of furniture remained and most of the pictures and vases and ornaments were gone, along with the rugs and standard lamps.

I then walked outside to find a large For Sale sign by the front gate, advertising the house and farm. Neglect was apparent at every turn in the garden. The lawns were overgrown, the pond full of decaying leaves. The maze had grown into one great bushy mass, the topiary animals no longer distinguishable. The caravan alone was as it had been. The kneehole desk and chair were there, as were the George Eliot and Tolstoy novels lining one shelf and Alexis's files on the other. On closer inspection I saw that everything was mouldy with damp. In a small cupboard I found the one bar electric fire Alexis had bought and I plugged it into a socket beside the shelves.

I knew what had happened but I was distressed by the

sight of the abandoned house and the state of the garden. As I sat gazing out of the leaded windows I saw my grandfather, a small squat figure standing by the entrance of the topiary maze. He was looking in my direction but did not appear to see me. He seemed immeasurably sad. And then the house disappeared and the scene changed.

Alexis was standing at the end of a seaside pier and there was no-one else in sight. He was wearing a light raincoat over his velvet smoking jacket and he was looking around in every direction. The structures of the pier, the old photographic kiosks and pavilions, were dilapidated. He ran his hand through thin grey hair which was receding and began to hum quietly. He was smoking a cigar which glowed and faded in the darkness, and was nearly extinguished by the slight breeze that was getting up. He looked down at the sea below him. The waves were tipped with foam and a half-moon cast its light on Alexis's melancholy face.

He turned to gaze at the sea for a while with an expression of deep gloom and then looked toward the Georgian façade that lined the sea-front. Dusk was on the cusp of night. He studied the beach to the right of him, where he could just make out a small red kite clinging to the breakwater. There were a few deckchairs, some blown over onto their sides. He closed his eyes and imagined a very different scene. Men were shouting, 'Bring in the boats! Bring them in! It's too rough to take them out – haul to, haul to!' There was a man with a telescope but he was not using it. Two women were strolling along, regardless of the seawater drenching the hems of their dresses, one holding a rolled up umbrella. A boy sitting on a barrel was singing a sea shanty about a whaler gone missing. From a creel a catch of flat-fish spilled over the pebbles. Above his head storm clouds were shot through with long fingers of sunlight, tracing and stroking the green-blue sea.

Alexis was calling to mind every detail of his painting. He saw the whole picture as he had never seen it before. I stood by him, invisible, and I could hear my grandfather's thoughts as though they were being spoken. He had shown the masterpiece to so many guests at The Grange, he had grown a little weary of the speeches he made on each occasion. Such freshness and power! The scene that was the closest to his heart would soon be sold to the highest bidder in London, along with the rest of his collection, and there would be nothing left.

He sighed. So much hurt he had brought on his family. The Grange, the farm and all the new equipment, the paintings, the many, many luxuries – they were all gone. What were paintings after all, beside his beloved Hazel and Vasili who had washed their hands of him? The bankruptcy had come like a thief in the night, this summer of 1949, not long after the second Aldeburgh Festival which he had helped to organise. Bailiffs were calling at all the hours of day and night and creditors were breathing down his neck, so one day he had risen early in the morning, packed a small suitcase and left it all behind. Three months had passed and it was autumn already.

Tomorrow at dawn he would fly out of England with his beautiful mistress, May. He had been seeing May for many years and he had bought a flat for the two of them. She had been his patient fifteen years ago and they had fallen very much in love at first sight. He had kept May a secret from Hazel and Vasili and when they moved to The Grange, it had been easy to meet her on Fridays when he was seeing his patients at Portland Place.

When the bankruptcy came crashing down on his head, he had fled to the Prince of Wales Drive in Battersea, where dear May lived in their comfortable flat. Now they must leave the country. He could not live without May. He could not live without Hazel and Vasili, but he had chosen May.

Only last week Hazel had written to him very courteously, saying she would have him back if he gave up his mistress. They could weather the bankruptcy together, she said, and forget the past. Vasili, though, would not speak to his father. Alexis hoped that Jane, his son's pretty wife, would persuade him to be more forgiving. Jane came from a farming family and had an open look about her that boded well for some kind of reconciliation with Vasili.

Alexis opened his eyes. It was very dark. The old chain pier, he knew, was blown away by a violent storm in the winter of 1896. It had been destroyed, with only a tiny piece of the structure remaining. Another pier, the one he stood on now, took its place not long after. An elderly guest at a soirée told Alexis that on the old pier there had been a silhouette artist, who made full-length portraits of visitors with a pair of scissors. Alexis pulled himself up to his full height. He must make plans.

Once he was in Europe he would seek out the White Russian émigrés who had known his own family. During his time in England he had not mixed with Russians, refusing invitations to parties and dinners, but in his hour of need they might help him. He could surely manage to raise the money to pay back the big Five, those great banks who had believed in him, as he believed in them. They had very kindly loaned him money over and over again, until everything fell down on his head. Alexis bowed his head in shame and then began to walk back down the pier. May was waiting for him at their hotel on the front. He walked quickly and kept his eyes straight in front of him.

I sat on in the caravan at The Grange. It was dark so I turned on the electric light, a single bulb over my head.

****

Meg put down her pen. She was very tired. *Chain Pier* had always had a strong hold on her imagination, even though as a girl she only knew the painting by reputation. Her mother would talk of a very big and grand picture but did not describe it to Meg in any detail, and her father never wanted to talk about it. Back then she had dreamt up a stormy sea and everything on the beach being blown away, swimming costumes and food for picnics, sandwiches and bananas littering the beach.

Ten years ago she had viewed the picture for the first time at the Tate and since then she had been back to look at it on many occasions. Meg looked at her watch. It was six in the morning. She went to bed and slept till late afternoon. When she woke the sun was streaming in through her bedroom window and she found herself fully clothed, apart from her shoes. After a bath, she heated some croissants, prepared some strong coffee and put on a dressing-gown and slippers.

By early evening she was ready to return to the past. She sat in her armchair looking out at a blood-red sunset that almost filled the small bay window.

Alexis and May had flown out of the country the day after their visit to Brighton. They had then disappeared for nearly two years, but one autumn day in 1951 Alexis was recognised by an Interpol officer in Lyons and arrested. The newspapers had reported sightings of them in various parts of the world – France, Switzerland, South Africa and even South America. They had kept moving on to avoid being caught and Alexis had visited Russian families, the great and the good, in every city they passed through, paying his way with his services as a doctor and massage specialist.

Early in January 1952, the year after Alexis was arrested, Hazel died. He would hear of her death in a South London prison cell, where he was awaiting his appeal (he was serving a nine-month sentence). Hazel was only sixty-six. She had left The Grange, when it was put up for sale shortly after the bankruptcy was declared, and had returned to London, where she lived in Highgate until her death following several strokes.

The funeral had taken place at a North London crematorium and Vasili estimated there were close on two hundred people lining the pews and standing at the back of the chapel. As the principal mourners, he and Jane sat closest to the altar and Hazel's coffin. Jane cradled Andrew, then a baby, shuddering with light *petit mals*. Fortunately the fits had not been too severe that day.

Before the service began, Vasili kept scanning the congregation. Several cousins and their families were there. He had lost touch with most of his relations. Work, marriage and a very sick child took up all of his time. Many of the mourners he did not recognise. He imagined a good percentage was made up of Hazel's fellow workers and former patients and their families. Yesterday one of his mother's colleagues rang to let him know there was to be a plaque commemorating Hazel's work at The Free and her teaching at The London School of Medicine for Women.

Vasili spotted a well-known actor who had been a neighbour and friend in Portland Place. He had trained with Hazel and Alexis for their pilots' licences at the Stag Lane airfield. Vasili could not be persuaded to take to the air but he'd join them for the day and watch from the field. High up in the London sky, his parents and the actor were tiny specks, swooping and dipping and lunging inside their machines. He recognised a few of the London Aeroplane Club people who had been for lunch a couple of times, and there was one of his parents' art dealer friends at the back of the chapel. He was to stand character witness at his father's appeal.

The light and airy Italianate chapel was packed beneath the high gabled rafters. Vasili was moved by how many people had come to pay their respects. Most of the mourners were seated or standing quietly when the chapel door opened and Alexis walked in between two tall men built like oxes. He was handcuffed to one of the warders and wearing prison clothes of drab grey. He had not set eyes on Vasili or Hazel for over two years and Vasili was struck by how haggard he looked.

The warders accompanied Alexis up the wide central aisle to sit along the pew from Vasili and Jane. One of the guards unlocked his handcuffs and Alexis sat with his head bowed, a forlorn figure. Vasili nearly leapt up to shout at his father to get out but Jane touched his knee to restrain him.

After Alexis was arrested in France three months ago, May had written to Vasili and Jane that he was in prison and in the process of appealing against his nine-month sentence. Jane had replied against her husband's wishes as she was hopeful for a reconciliation.

The service began. It was as Hazel wished, brief and to the point. She and Alexis had held to their Anglican faith but found little time to attend church, and Vasili, an atheist, and Jane, an agnostic, were glad it would be over soon. It was a relief that Andrew would not have to sit still for long. There was a short address by the vicar. The flowers outside and the many glowing obituaries in the newspapers were enough. Vasili had been reading them out to Jane over breakfast each morning for the past week.

Vasili and Alexis cried quietly, unfolding large white handkerchiefs to dry their eyes. Alexis had wished for a meeting with Hazel, but she had refused to the end. He glanced along the pew. There was room for at least two mourners between himself and his son, who sat with his eyes in front of him, refusing to acknowledge his father. When the service was over, Alexis walked out of the pew and around by the altar, where he turned to face Vasili and Jane. Vasili got up and walked away but Jane smiled at her father-in-law. One of the warders stood behind their prisoner to keep a close eye on him. Alexis could have a few minutes but that was all.

Alexis knew from May about the child's epilepsy as she was in contact with Jane by letter. He greeted Jane warmly and then, gazing down at Andrew, expressed his deep regret that his grandson was so very ill. The warder had secured the handcuffs to Alexis's left wrist, but he was able to place his free hand, palm down, on Andrew's head, holding it there for the duration of his talk with Jane. 'Perhaps when I am freed from prison, I might give the little one treatment, my dear.' Jane was touched by his words and wished that Vasili was not so obstinate and dismissive of his father. She thanked Alexis and hoped that they might see him in the not too distant future.

'Andrew. Andrew. Andrew.' With his strong square hand on the child's damaged head, Alexis chanted the name of his grandson, as if he were a priest, and then turned to Jane again.

'And you are pregnant with another little one, I believe? Do you hope for a little girl?'

'I don't mind, Dr. Chodak, boy or girl. The baby's due in June, a few weeks after Andrew's birthday.' Jane paused for a moment. 'I am so sorry about your troubles. I do hope the appeal is successful. I would love you to come and see us, but I'm not sure Vasili will agree. He needs time.'

The warder told Alexis his time was up and, with great regret, he kissed Jane goodbye. He hoped the next birth would be much easier than the first. He would pray for her. Slowly he removed his hand from Andrew's head and kissed the sleeping child farewell.

'Goodbye, my little one. Until we meet again and may that not be so long.'

Alexis was driven away in the prison van. There were reports of 'Dr. Chodak' proving very popular with his fellow inmates and warders, to whom he gave massages in a corner of the prison yard. He sung folk songs while he worked and his patients gathered around like disciples.

****

Meg imagined her grandfather in his cell. His face was lit by a candle procured for him by one of the warders. He preferred candlelight to the bald bulb of electric light. When he was sitting on the thin mattress of the prison bed, his head bowed, did he at last see the boy he once was? Meg wondered. Did he come face to face with the boy who could not bear to look back? Did he feel that he had betrayed his family and their legacy?

She tried to see through her grandfather's eyes. There was Tati with her mischievous smile, holding her brother's hand, as if all she had ever needed was her elder brother. There was his family sitting and standing in the large music room in the dacha. They had assembled after their evening meal to dance and sing, and that fresh faced boy playing the balalaika was surely Alexis. Everyone was lining up in two rows that faced each other – his parents, Alexander and Catherine, his sisters and brothers, Sophia, Katerina, Mary and Nicholas, and some family friends. They were clapping their hands in time to the music, and the dancers were bobbing forward and back, and there was Alexis dancing down the middle of the lines with Tati. Perhaps in prison, with more time on his hands, her grandfather had been able to recall the past with more clarity.

Alexis won his appeal, on the strength of the testimony of his character witnesses and owing to some of his former patients clubbing together to pay off the remainder of his debts (amounting in the region of £10,000). He went on to establish a smaller medical practice in London and remained with May until he died in 1964.

9

The pond

The South London prison, where Meg's grandfather spent some months, was not far from where she lived. She did not often pass it, but sometimes at the weekend she walked to a market and the route took her by the prison gates. Her pace would quicken as she drew near and she barely glimpsed the visitors waiting outside. She would hold her breath, as if she herself were in danger of being incarcerated.

Prisons had been a preoccupation with Meg for much of her life. At the Tate Gallery once, a doorman told Meg that the gallery stood on the foundations of a Victorian prison. 'They're still below us,' he had laughed, gazing down at his feet. Meg wondered if he had ever been in prison himself. Her father had often visited patients in prison, to decide whether they should be in a psychiatric hospital instead. As senior consultant and administrator at the largest of the cluster of mental hospitals in Epsom, these decisions gave him a headache. His wards were already bursting at the seams. He hated the sight of these men languishing in gaol, though, and invariably signed the papers for their transfer to the hospital.

All those bed-sitting rooms and small apartments Meg had rented prior to buying her current flat reminded her of prison cells. She had often chosen the smallest, most uncomfortable spaces to live in, as if she had no choice in the matter. She was beginning to see the extent to which she had imprisoned herself in these rooms.

Andrew and Meg. Meg and Andrew. The baby boy Jane had cradled in her arms at Hazel's funeral, bore little relationship to the man that Andrew became. In photographs of Andrew and herself as children, she could see that her affection for him was clear, along with her compassion. She recognised the tenderness in her eyes and also the flicker of anxiety as she sat beside him. Early on in their sibling lives she had loved her brother absolutely. Andrew's eyes were always blurred with medicine and Meg wondered if she had misread his look all her life. It was beginning to dawn on her that Andrew was in a permanent haze, which was punctuated by the relentless *petit mals*. He had no time to take her in. She was the one who had watched with clear eyes.

Meg had always liked Andrew's name. Andrew sounded strong and natural like taking a deep breath. Her own name, Meg, she was less sure of. It seemed fragile and unsure, as if about to take breath but deciding not to after all.

Midnight. She realised she was up for another night, but she must sit this out. Food. She needed food. Having scrambled some eggs and fried mushrooms and tomatoes, she fetched a bottle of chilled lager from the fridge and poured herself a glass of water, which she drank straight off. She ate slowly and then got up to look outside. The night was mild and she pulled up the sash window in the bay. There was a man beneath some trees, whistling, and then a dog barked and raced up beside him, licking the man's hand and giving his body a shake – a golden retriever. Oblivious of Meg studying their night walk, the man and his dog moved on toward the bandstand.

Alexis had placed his hand on Andrew's head in the chapel. Meg sat down to resume the work of memory, jotting down a word or two, a phrase, a sentence.

1968

Meg, aged sixteen, stood outside the breakfast room door. It was mid October and mild for the time of year. 'Ha! Ha! Ha!' Andrew's laugh was a hard guffaw. The happier giggling of his childhood had disappeared. Eighteen now, he sounded as if he was driving nails into a wall. Meg watched Andrew and her father laughing together at a silent film on the television. Vasili's laughter was contained, careful, and every so often he would glance at Andrew as if on tenterhooks. They couldn't see Meg and for a while she remained by the door, glad that they were laughing and hoping the moment might last forever. She did not consider joining them, firstly because she was not that keen on silent movies, and secondly, she relished the sense of freedom that suddenly swept over her as she watched. Andrew was safe with her father, even happy.

The little man in a bowler hat walked quickly across the screen, swaying from side to side, and then he tripped up and fell flat on his face. He seemed very alone and yet everywhere he went people noticed him – bumping into people, getting in their way, causing accidents. Meg loved the look and the idea of Charlie Chaplin, but she did not find the film funny in the way Andrew and Vasili did. When Chaplin fell over they thought it was hilarious. Meg was more relieved by his endless ability to get back onto his feet.

Andrew was not answering to 'Andrew' at present. His name was Rasputin, he had told everyone last week, and they were to address him as such. When Meg asked her history teacher about Rasputin, she told Meg as much as she knew – the monk advised Alexandra, the Tsar Nicholas's wife, and claimed to be a faith healer and a prophet. The teacher concluded, 'He was a terrible man, an evil man, with a long beard and mad, evil eyes. He was epileptic and believed he spoke with God when he was having a seizure.'

Meg had wondered if her teacher knew Andrew was epileptic.

Andrew was now an imposing figure – solidly built with a square, determined jaw. He often went bare-footed and wore a monk's habit, which he had made himself. Strolling along the parade of village shops, he would bless the people who crossed his path.

Meg longed for someone to blame for her brother's illness. That question was forever on the prowl, waiting in a corner ready to pounce. The doctor was guilty, the man who had mistakenly applied the forceps to Andrew's brain, but he was lost in the distant past. She wanted to haul someone up here and now to account for the accident.

Her mother seemed to take Andrew's illness in her stride, even when he lost touch with reality and either preached or raged. Meg was still standing by the breakfast room door. Her father and Andrew watching a silent movie was the most natural thing in the world. And yet, only a month or two back Andrew had built an altar to the devil in his bedroom, with pictures of demons, black candles and plasticine figures with nails stuck into them, crowding the altar. In the dead of night everyone could hear Andrew chanting his imprecations. One day he was Christ, the next Satan. Today he was Rasputin. Tomorrow he might be Andrew again.

Sometimes he sounded just like Andrew. At breakfast a couple of weeks ago he had almost skipped into the breakfast room. 'Mum, Dad, Meg. Yesterday Jesus appeared in a blaze of light beside the Willow Café and, in front of all the old birds drinking tea, I swore to love and obey the Lord! My mission is to convert you all, you sinners!' He had then gathered up the altar and fetishes, along with his shelf of Dennis Wheatley's Satanic novels, and made a huge bonfire of them in the garden. Meg smiled. She could admire the surreal, if chilling, humour Andrew mustered in the face of his suffering.

Meg continued to stand by the door, staring at the flickering television screen. Chaplin's odd little figure reassured her. She wished there was a silent film running in every room of the house. This would keep Andrew occupied and happy. Meg often woke to find her brother in her bedroom, gazing down at her as she opened her eyes, and then he'd grin before stomping out and banging the door behind him so her bedroom shook. Yesterday he filmed her in bed with his cine-camera as she was waking up.

It had occurred to Meg that she might buy a lock from the ironmongers in the village and fix it to her door, but no, she must face Andrew square on without fear. She must accommodate him. That was the only reasonable thing to do. Meg's rational mind was completely out of step with her other mind, which lived in all kinds of places – deep inside woods with the elves or in among the sea grass on ocean beds.

The silent movie had finished and Meg's heart sank. What next?

She went up to her bedroom to read some chapters of the Thomas Hardy novel she was studying for 'A' Level. She had nearly finished the book and had just resumed reading when Andrew kicked her door open. He was in his old jeans and no longer in his Rasputin habit. He was wearing an enormous Mexican sombrero, which he had ordered a few months ago from South America. He was also carrying his air-gun, which he kept hidden from Vasili and Jane, but not from Meg. He took pot shots at birds and cats from his bedroom window.

'I'm goin' up the shops. Comin'?'

Meg did not answer but closed the Hardy and stood up. She was embarrassed to be seen with Andrew wearing his sombrero, but admired the defiance that insisted on outlandishness in the face of the stockbrokers and their wives in the village. As they walked past the railway station into the line of shops, Andrew gave Meg her instructions.

'I'm goin' to put on a Mexican accent. You mustn't speak.

You're dumb, you're my dumb sister.'

Miss Smith's was the first shop they arrived at. It was on a corner and faced the station entrance. The shop sold ladies' dresses and nylons with seams up the back, along with a range of woollen underwear and sewing materials. In the window there were flat shoes with laces on display and school uniforms.

When Andrew and Meg walked in, Miss Smith, an elderly woman with an air of grey weariness, recognised the strange Chodak children. She was taken aback by the huge felt sombrero in bottle green, with its red trimming round the high pointed crown. Andrew had tilted the hat over his face so you could not see his eyes. Meg gazed at her brother. His long hair and beard had the aspect of a desperado from the television series, *Bonanza*. He might have been about to engage in a shoot-out with one of the cowboys, who lived on a huge ranch called The Ponderosa. She liked Little Joe, who was mischievous and good-looking.

'Mees Smeef, 'allo, ow ara youa? I wanna de neelons for me sister who canno speak – comprenez?'

Miss Smith looked nervous. She knew Andrew and Meg, as they came into the shop with Jane regularly, but she was clearly taken aback by Andrew's request. Her brother was looking into the distance and Meg knew he was having a series of light *petit mals*. The tremor that rippled through his body was imperceptible to most people, who thought Andrew was day-dreaming, simply miles away. Meg wanted to explain to Miss Smith that her brother was having silent fits and that she could hear pins dropping all around her and 'Ring-a-ring-a-roses' playing in the background. We all fall down. We all fall down.

Andrew swayed slightly and the sombrero fell off. Meg picked it up and her brother snatched it back the instant he came to. He glanced about him, angry and disconcerted. The make-believe was over. He and Meg walked out of the shop, leaving Miss Smith looking relieved.

The siblings stood on the pavement outside. Meg hoped Andrew would want to return home but, no, he wished to buy a pineapple at the greengrocers, Oakleys, a few shops along. They walked past the ladies hairdressers and into Oakleys. Meg scanned the apples, oranges, pears, pineapples and clusters of black grapes on display. Andrew picked out the largest and ripest pineapple and placed it inside the pointed crown of his sombrero, and then glanced over at Meg, as if to say, 'Keep your mouth shut!'

Mr Oakley walked over. He knew Andrew well, as he had worked in the shop on Saturday mornings a couple of years ago, but he'd had to let him go. The fits came once too often and put off the customers, and anyway, his insurance wouldn't cover him. He'd told Meg's mother it was a shame as Andrew was a hard worker. The next minute Andrew was falling through the air, the pineapple flying out of the sombrero as his arms shot out each side of him in a massive *grand mal*. He crashed down against one of the displays and landed on his back, his body splayed out on the floor of the small shop.

This was the first time Meg had witnessed a *grand mal*. She knew from her parents that Andrew bit down hard on his tongue so it bled, and that he wet himself, but nothing had prepared her for this. Her brother was jerking violently on the floor. She could see his teeth chomping his tongue and blood was pouring out of his mouth. She smelled the urine that was trickling onto the floor and everyone in the shop was staring at her, like she knew what to do but she didn't.

To see Andrew like this – she could not bear it. He was snorting and flailing about. The urine was spreading all over the ground, like juice from the fruits, in a huge yellow stain. The people were still turned towards her, unmoving as statues, reproaching her, blaming her for not helping her brother. That's his sister, their eyes said. Meg gazed down at Andrew. His arms were wide open like he was beseeching her to understand his terrible predicament. My God, my God, Meg, Meg, why hast thou forsaken me? Why, why, why?

Meg rushed out of the shop and away from Andrew and all the people gathered round his body – expecting her to do something. She ran and ran as if the devil were at her back. Alexis. Alexis. Alexis was at her side. They were running for their lives. And then he disappeared and Meg was on her own. She felt like she was sprinting on the spot, the exact spot where Andrew landed with such an almighty crunch. She was tearing along at speed. Had he broken anything? Up the alley (voices screeching at her on either side, huge dogs looming in the gardens at the back of the houses, dog-breath in her mouth, angry eyes, sharp teeth at the point of sinking into her flesh) and out and away across the heath she sped toward the duck pond in the adjacent village.

At the edge of the pond she stopped. Meg sat down on one of the benches to take breath. She gazed at the ducks. Behind her the rust red of autumn leaves. A girl sitting by a duck pond, the most natural thing in the world. Meg realised she must confess to her parents, tell them of the terrible crime she had committed, the crime of leaving Andrew alone on the shop floor. He might be dead by now. She had left her brother for dead and Alexis had left his family for dead.

Meg stayed by the pond for a few minutes before jumping up to race back over the heath. She knew this rough ground very well. She and Andrew played houses in among the clearings. Out into the avenue and on down the alley that took her back to the shops.

Alexis, a fourteen year old boy again, was at her side and barely out of breath. He'd run all the way from Tashkent to be with Meg in her trouble. She wished she could be like him and never go back. Her parents' voices filled her head – 'This is life, Meg, it's hard but you have to get on with it. You are more fortunate than many.'

Nowhere to run, nowhere to hide. Meg sped down the slope toward the petrol pumps and past the postal sorting office. She ran across the road, a car narrowly missing her.

She raced up the pavement toward Holmwood, past the convent and up the short drive, past the line of hydrangeas, and at last she opened the front door and found herself inside the house.

Mr Oakley had by this time rung Jane, who had collected Andrew in the car. He was in bed where he would sleep deeply, on the cusp of death, for twelve hours or more; and then he would wake to the searing pain of his chewed up tongue, blood still leaking from his mouth and drying on his beard in dark clots. For the next couple of weeks Andrew would only be able to sip tepid soups, cool porridge and warm ice-cream. How could her brother live with his illness?

Meg ran into her bedroom and refused to come out. She was guilty and there was nothing anyone could say that would help. It wasn't your fault. It's understandable you were frightened. No. She should have been there to help her brother. Running off like that was unforgivable. Scaredy-cat, scaredy-cat! Voices from all sides hissed and jeered. The silent film, Andrew and her father watching Charlie Chaplin. No good, that was many moons ago. No good. Nothing helps. Nothing matters. Meg had declared herself guilty, guilty, guilty as charged.

****

Several weeks later, when Andrew had recovered, he set to work on something he was making upstairs in the big attic. This was occasionally used as a spare room and two camp beds were folded up and propped against the wall. In the summer Andrew and Meg had painted all the walls dark pink, with the exception of the wall facing the door, which was a deep shade of purple.

Andrew forbade his family to enter the attic for the duration of his work. He bought bolts and a Chubb lock from the hardware shop in the village and secured the bolts on the inside of the door. He then fitted the Chubb and, after a day's work, he locked the room on the outside. Meg, Jane and Vasili could hear him hammering and sawing, drilling and sandpapering, and lugging large items about overhead. Andrew appeared at mealtimes, when he wolfed down his food and left the table early to get back on the job. There was a bounce in his step and a glint of steely determination in his pale blue eyes. Calm reigned in the house during this period. Things were not so bad after all, Meg reflected.

She was reading another Thomas Hardy novel. This one was about a small boy, nicknamed 'Old Father Time', who carried the weight of the world on his shoulders. She was also reading Tennyson's long poem, mourning the death of his friend at an early age. Love and loss. She wished she could lock herself in like Andrew did, so she might read day and night.

On the third day Andrew appeared in the drawing-room after dinner. It was a cold night in November and the open fire was lit, the wood crackling in the grate. Meg was sitting on the carpet by the fireplace, resting her head against one of the big armchairs each side of the hearth. The chair was comfortably battered with age and in need of new springs. Vasili was playing some Chopin preludes with slow deliberation.

Jane sat on the long beige and brown sofa facing the fire. She was sewing a tapestry of roses to cover the piano stool. They were all three about to watch the television adaptation of *The Forsyte Saga*, which was being repeated. Meg had loved the drama, but she had missed some of the episodes and was looking forward to watching the series again.

The story was of an upper middle class family, whose complex and interwoven relationships were played out over three generations. Even though her concentration was poor and her studying of anything sporadic and intermittent, she liked to believe she could follow the plot through from beginning to end. She had begun studying for 'A' Levels and beside the fire she was reading *Middlemarch*. Unlike Hardy's novels, where individuals are alone in their lives and tragic, fated figures, this book by George Eliot held out the possibility that connections within a wide circle might help a person bear life's pain and disappointment.

Her book was lying open on the floor, the pages covered with her pencilled annotations. She was sprawled out and stretching her legs when Andrew entered, kicking the solid door open, so it battered the wall. Meg jumped. There were dents in every single door in the house, where Andrew had kicked them. The latches broke frequently. Her novel was suddenly unimportant, the book a million miles away.

'Andrew, *please* will you kindly not kick the door like that. It'll come off its hinges one day!'

Jane looked up at her son, her needle and thread poised in mid-air. Vasili stopped playing abruptly and closed the piano lid with a slight bang, as if to say, 'Well, that's that for this evening.' Meg went to sit in the armchair to make some space for Andrew by the fire. Her brother began to stoke the coals to a blaze with the poker, threatening to set the chimney alight.

'Andrew, *don't* stoke it up like that!'

This time Vasili spoke without conviction and sat down wearily next to Jane on the sofa. He and Jane were beginning to give up on the idea that some kind of solution might be found for their son. Andrew grinned over at his parents. The fire was in a fury of flames as he faced them, with Meg to one side of him and not in his full gaze.

'I have an announcement to make!'

'Andrew, we're about to watch *The Forsyte Saga*. Couldn't it wait till afterwards?'

Jane sighed. There was her troubled son, all six feet and more of him, looming over her, his big strong legs wide apart in front of the fire. The backs of his legs would be burning. She had lost count of the pairs of jeans that had been badly singed by Andrew standing so close to the fire. And then his arms shot out each side of him and he swayed and jerked in a fit, with the fire roaring behind him. Vasili sat forward, ready to catch Andrew should he fall and they all waited patiently, praying the fits would not tip over into a *grand mal*. Meg had forgotten all about the series, the story, the characters' names, the plot – they all escaped her. Forget it. Why bother reading and watching television series? Rubbish. They were rubbish.

Andrew was silent for a minute or so after the *petit mal* finished. He was trying to remember why he came into the drawing-room in the first place.

Everyone waited until Andrew managed to pick up his train of thought. When at last it came to him, he might have been lifting, high up into the air, one of the shiny Dinky toys of his childhood. He was ecstatic when he recollected where he was and smiled indulgently at his family.

'Tomorrow evening in the attic, folks, I am giving a performance and I expect you three to be there. It is a one man show called *The Upright Man*. Please take your seats by eight pm. So long.'

Andrew banged the door behind him. They would be able to watch *The Forsyte Saga* after all. But to enjoy it would be a betrayal. Meg's memory of the series slowly returned, the anticipated episodes stretching out in front of her through the winter months. One after another after another. Twenty-six episodes. She must watch them all.

****

On the way up to the attic there was a framed picture of a huge green circle, composed of a mass of lines criss-crossing each other in perfect symmetry. Andrew had taken two days, a couple of summers ago, to draw this circle with his green biro and compass. Meg had watched her brother tracing the circle and the lines that seemed to have no beginning or end, a vortex arriving miraculously at a pinprick of white in the centre of the sphere. She was amazed at Andrew's drawing, envied him his application to the task.

The previous year Meg had been chastised by the art

teacher at school for being 'incapable of drawing a straight line' and Meg asked if she might instead sit at the back of the class, where she could do some 'abstract paintings'. She was no good at drawing trees lining roads that stretched away into the distance. Her Uncle Laurie had talked to her about abstract pictures and how you could 'take a line for a walk'. He gave lectures at the Tate Gallery and drew pictures with swirling lines and dots and splashes, which illustrated the front covers of the *Radio Times*.

The teacher agreed to Meg's suggestion but turned up her nose at the idea of 'abstract painting'. Relegated to the back of the class, not quite in a corner, Meg produced a picture that glowed with pink, purple, blue and green pyramids and lines and splodges in thickly mixed watercolours. She imagined she was a famous abstract painter but hot on the heels of that idea, she became a patient in her father's hospital. Her father's patients did 'abstract painting' to help them express their feelings. Where had that painting of hers got to? Meg wondered.

The attic, with its pink and purple walls, was a large L-shaped room. The short part of the L began by the door and the long bit was big enough for the table tennis table, stored in the tiny box room next door. Meg was very good at table tennis. She could hit the back edge of the table so that the ball dropped dead to the ground, which meant her opponent had no time to return it, unless their eye was as fine as hers and their reactions as lightning quick.

Andrew opened the door with a flourish, ushering in his parents and his sister.

'Come in, come in folks, and make yourselves at home.'

He was dressed in a full cowboy outfit he had ordered from Texas. This consisted of a large black stetson, a bright yellow bandana which he wore around his neck, strong leather cowboy boots with pointed toes and heels, leather chaps for his legs and deerskin gloves. The tight faded Levis were Andrew's own. He wore a holster round his hips, into which he had tucked his air gun, which his parents thought was a toy gun. Only Meg knew it was real. Andrew chuckled to himself. To complete the outfit he had donned a large fake moustache he bought in a joke shop in London when Vasili took him for one of his appointments at the National.

There were four chairs in a row. The fourth place was for any of the cats if they strayed in during the performance. Andrew asked for the door to be kept ajar, so that the cats could 'come and go as they pleased'. Meg had wondered if he would lock them in and throw away the key and she breathed more freely. Andrew had rigged up a pink velvet curtain which was drawn in front of the stage. The curtains in the small attic window facing the stage, were also closed, so when Andrew switched off the light the family sat in the dark.

From behind the curtain Andrew shouted, 'Let the show begin! This is the tale of *The Upright Man!*' You could hear him striking matches and, when he pulled the curtain back, there was Andrew sitting at the centre of the stage surrounded by lots of large candles lighting up the scene.

He had constructed the large wooden stage from pieces of plain wood, which he bought from a local timber merchants. The wood was screwed to the floor and held together perfectly, with the finished, sand-papered stage standing a good eight inches from the floor. Andrew was sat in an upright coffin he had also constructed for the performance. This was made of a rougher and thicker wood than the stage. He had built a loudspeaker into the top of the coffin and, to get it to stand up, had screwed the coffin firmly into the stage. Behind the construction there was a heavy packing trunk from the box room to support Andrew's weight when he sat down.

In the middle of the coffin Andrew had inserted the seat and there he sat, peering out into the gloom which held his family, through colored plastic streamers. Tiny, the slim black cat with a tiny dot of white on her throat, was sitting in Jane's lap and not on the spare seat provided for her. Andrew parted the streamers, attaching them to the side of the coffin with a large bulldog clip.

'Welcome all. We are gathered here today to witness the performance of *The Upright Man*. I act as the Upright Man and will play some songs, accompanying them on my guitar. I am like Johnny Cash, I'm a travelling player. This evening I am in Surrey, tomorrow I will be in Vegas! I designed the stage set myself.'

Andrew sat in the coffin playing his acoustic guitar, stumbling over the chords but managing to hold the tune. He began to sing *The Upright Man* to the tune of Stevie Wonder's *Uptight:*

Baby, everything is all right
Upright I'm in the attic outta sight

I'm a rich shrink's son from across the railway tracks
Every shirt I own is hanging on my back
I know I'm not the average kind of guy
I'm from a big old house with my family

my, my

It's alright...upright...

Andrew sang well. Vasili and Jane didn't know the Stevie Wonder song but they admired their son's voice and ingenuity. What could they and Meg do in the face of such an extraordinary statement as this? Andrew had made the coffin as a huge joke, a surreal comment on his life so far. Meg laughed out loud at her brother's wit and nerve. Whenever she had volunteered to act in school plays, she had always chickened out at the last moment. The thought of everyone's eyes on her was too much – even playing a piano duet with a friend in front of the school was beyond her. She had frozen and her friend went on to play her half of the duet, while Meg sat trembling and blushed scarlet. She could play the piano reasonably well on her own, but in front of an audience it was impossible.

Upright. Out of sight. Genius. Her brother was a genius. After the song Andrew asked for requests. Jane chose The Beatles' *Yesterday*, the song she had heard her son playing in his bedroom. Yes, it looked as though her son's troubles were *here to stay. Suddenly I'm not half the man I used to be.* And nor am I, thought Vasili. He, 'the shrink', had failed Andrew and could do nothing in the face of this ghastly illness. *There's a shadow hanging over me, oh yesterday came suddenly.* There was always a shadow hanging over Meg's brother and the fits arrived out of the blue. Sudden as thunder and lightning. Sudden as rain. Sudden. Sudden. Meg sang along with Andrew in an undertone.

He played several requests – another one of his mother's, *Ol' Man River* and *Here, There and Everywhere* for Meg. Vasili couldn't think of a request and Andrew sneered at his father's ignorance. Meg could see that her father was longing to return to the drawing-room, the piano and *The Third Programme* for his classical music. Andrew grinned at Vasili and finished playing with a loud strum, after which he announced there was to be an interval of ten minutes. Andrew then handed round glasses of orange squash he had prepared and a box of *Quality Street* chocolates. Meg, Vasili and Jane ate silently and waited for the performance to resume.

After the interval Andrew left the stage and walked over to the large drum kit by the small and only window in the room. For fifteen minutes he battered the drums and crashed the cymbals, emulating Keith Moon of The Who. Ablaze with the rhythms, he pounded the drums, bashed and bashed the cymbals until the drumsticks flew out of his hands in a *petit mal*.

His family froze in their seats and everything went quiet until Andrew came round, and then it was as if his performance, the songs and the drum solo had never happened. He stood up and announced, 'I'm off to kip folks. See yourselves out,' and slammed the door behind him. The room shook beneath his family's feet. How predictable the scene was. Meg would have been surprised to learn that her parents were, like her, experiencing a keen sense of déjà vu.

A week later Andrew was admitted to one of the psychiatric hospitals in Epsom, not his father's, but a small hospital for short stay patients experiencing acute symptoms. Andrew had surprised his family by admitting himself voluntarily. He was diagnosed as suffering from 'epilepsy with psychotic episodes'. Vasili and Jane visited their son every day but decided Meg should not join them. Meg was relieved. She didn't want to see Andrew in hospital. After a few days, though, she felt like half of her had been lopped off.

10

A glass of water

Dawn was breaking. Meg, who had been up all night, stood by the window and scanned the common, her eyes resting on the pond not far from her house, where some early morning anglers were casting their lines. When she was in her teens she'd often sat on the bench by the pond. She just sat there. Meg was beginning to feel more compassion for the distressed girl who thought she might explode with all the unspoken feelings.

As Andrew grew more acutely ill in his adolescence, she had retreated further into herself. She was amazed that after all these years those three damning letters still hovered above her head. 'B A D'. The letters floated in the air and she had little control over them.

Two years after Andrew strummed his guitar in the coffin, Meg had rushed to collect the post falling onto the doormat one morning. Her 'A' level results were due. She spotted the white envelope addressed to her and, leaving the rest of the post, ran up to her bedroom where, after counting to a hundred, she opened it. The grades were printed on a small postcard – 'B' for English, 'A' for History and 'D' for Latin. First she was happy, very happy, that she had passed all three, especially the Latin as she had done little work in the subject. Other than enjoying Virgil's poetry and his story of Aeneas descending into Hades, she had spent very little time on the subject. The reason she had passed with a

'D' was because the unseen translation (from Latin to English) was one they had, by pure chance, studied the term before. It was unbelievable luck.

The 'A' for history was deserved. She had memorised so much. They were only facts, though, and soon forgotten.

The 'B' for English was a big disappointment. It had been bad, very bad of her to neglect her favourite subject. Rote learning of historical facts had been so much easier than grappling with the passionate love and hatred and envy she had found in Shakespeare. B A D. The grades said it all.

Meg was shocked by the fact that the letters were still accompanying her two decades later. Time for some more sleep. She had gone to bed two mornings in a row. She wondered if the quality of your dreams changed if you worked nights regularly. Were they lit by the dawn sun glancing through the curtains?

She found it hard recalling her own dreams, except for the nightmares she had habitually between the age of sixteen and thirty-six or so. They were always the same. A man climbed through the window into her bedroom. He had come for her, and then she would suddenly leap out of bed, stifling her cries, and run to the window. At the point of pulling it open she woke.

Why had she run toward the window? Why not run away from the man and out of her door? In the dream she was not planning to jump out. Meg had a sudden, surprising thought. Maybe she had been desperate for some fresh air. As Meg got into bed, she felt something lighten in her. She spread out her arms and stretched. Daylight was filtering through the curtains, which were a pattern of soft turquoise, dusky pink and pale blue. The silky curtains were left by the couple, a sculptor and a florist, who had sold Meg the flat. They were the kind of curtains she might have dreamt up for herself in another life. She could not quite believe they were hers.

The dream of the man coming through the window had gradually become less frequent and then a few years ago it had stopped. Her right knee had stopped shaking at about the same time.

Meg slept well and woke at three in the afternoon. She went into the kitchen and poured herself a glass of ice-cold water.

Alexis and Andrew. Andrew and Alexis. These two boys, these two men, had preoccupied her for a very long time. Her parents and her friends had receded into the distance, fallen away. B A D – the letters were back again like a bad smell. What had happened after her 'A' Level results arrived in the summer of 1970? Meg wrote the three letters in large capitals on a sheet of paper which she placed on her desk. She then drew the curtains and opened the window. The trees on the common struck her as extraordinarily beautiful. Mature limes and oaks. She could just make out the bandstand among a cluster of trees. Some boys were fishing in the pond. There was a fund-raising concert for the bandstand renovation tomorrow afternoon and Meg was going to help out with one of the stalls.

She made some coffee and sat down at her desk.

B A D. Between passing her 'A' Levels in 1970 and settling by the common there were decades that came and went. The day after getting those results Meg found herself falling away from things badly. She let go of her known world, leaving home suddenly, like a thud in the night, to work on conveyor belts in factories on the Purley Way, where the women on the line swore at her for being clumsy and slow. Her job was to solder wires to the backs of televisions, but she burnt her fingers and got the wires muddled up.

After working in the factories she went to a university in one the home counties, which was a friendly place. Andrew came out of the psychiatric hospital in 1968 after a few months, but he grew more ill, and kept leaving home. He would set out before dawn in his monk's habit, telling his parents he was walking to Tashkent to see his relatives and bring them the word of God. He had met his grandfather's family in a vision. He would bring them word from their ancestor, Alexis. The police picked him up at the side of a dual carriageway.

'He was flat out, unconscious and his mouth was full of blood,' one policeman told Vasili and Jane.

In the third week of her first term at university, where she was studying History and not English, Jane rang Meg to let her know that Andrew was on his way to see her. He'd left a note. 'I'm going after Meg, folks. So long.' Andrew didn't arrive as he had a *grand mal* in a pub in Canterbury (a half pint of lager set off the fit) and an ambulance returned him home, along with a policeman, who was surprised his parents allowed such an ill young man to go off like that. 'We don't believe in wrapping Andrew up in cotton wool, officer. He must have a certain amount of freedom. We can't keep him under lock and key,' Vasili wearily told the policeman who stayed for a cup of tea.

Andrew coming for her was too hard to think about. Meg dropped out of university at the end of the term to move into a bedsit in London. She thought she was escaping her brother, but wherever she ran, he was around the next corner or sitting in the middle of the road waiting for her. Andrew was everywhere. He was her twin soul. They were siblings in arms up against the world. Meg dwelt in the darkness. She stopped reading and thinking and dancing and swimming. She sat in cinemas on her own, craving the litter beneath maroon velvet seats, discarded cigarette cartons, ice-cream wrappers and the bitter cigarette butts.

She got a job at a domed cinema in Notting Hill, where she became the dress circle usherette. Her job was to tear the punters' tickets and guide them with her torch into their seats in the steep auditorium. During the showing she sat on the carpeted steps. All she wanted to do was watch the film. She would wave her torch vaguely in the direction of the cinema goers, whilst appearing distant and bored. 'Find your own way,' she muttered to herself.

Meg missed the beginning of the film as she had to stand outside the door in case there were any latecomers. Fifteen minutes from the end she had to go downstairs to smile at the punters as they left the cinema, like they are our guests, the manager said. The film changed every fortnight and by the time Meg left the job four months later, she had seen eight films, but without ever seeing a beginning or an end. This struck her as in some way important, even witty, but she had no idea why.

Most of the films Meg grew tired of by the third or fourth showing but there was one she watched without becoming weary. This was the adaptation of Aleksandr Solzhenitsyn's *One Day in the Life of Ivan Denisovich*, a novella set in a Gulag labour camp in northern Kazakhstan. The film was about Ivan who worked on a construction site, bricklaying in the extreme cold. The mortar he used to lay the bricks froze if he did not apply it thickly enough. Ivan survived each gruelling day of his sentence.

Meg found the film strangely reassuring. Kazakhstan was in Central Asia, not far from where Alexis grew up. He'd run away and he'd survived the firing squad. Day followed day for Alexis. He bore a future in mind, even when things were very bad.

Meg kept on running.

She learned to type from a dictaphone tape, recorded by whoever was employing her at the time. Their names she forgot. All she needed to do was plug in for the day. She became a temporary secretary and spent well over a decade moving from job to job, beginning a new position every day or every week, depending on how long she was needed. Occasionally she was asked to stay on a semi-permanent basis, but that unsettled her and she'd hand in her notice. She understood, but did not take in what she was typing. Her English was superlative and she was a very fast typist, so after a while Meg was in demand.

By day she typed and by night she went to shady haunts, where she drank and danced and kissed and swayed with whoever drew her to him. Her body did not belong to her. She watched Bergman films endlessly, caught up in the tortuous cycles of sexual despair the Swedish director returned to again and again. The structures in her life fell away. The air grew thin. She binged on food and alcohol. Nothing was enough. Like Alice she ate and drank whatever appeared in front of her or, unlike Alice, she simply starved. She grew fat, she grew thin, she grew distorted. She dwindled. She loomed. She didn't cry.

One, almost two decades. They came and went. Meg whirled around and around till she grew giddy and nearly died. She plummeted, she fell, in an endless series of fits and starts that kept on and on repeating themselves. Andrew, Andrew, Andrew. *Petit mals, grand mals, petit mals, grand mals.* Once she had walked on her hands in a garden somewhere. Falling, falling, falling. Alexis's family stood in a line, facing their killers.

Lines were made to be broken, leaving jagged loose ends, frayed bits and pieces of thread. She was holding her father's hand. Where was her mother? Looking after Andrew, listening out for the thud in his bedroom. Her mother never got much sleep. Meg collapsed and grew small as the speck in her eye. 'The speck is pretty,' people said. Decades that barely constitute a chapter. That is all they add up to. Eyes dead and frantic by turns. Darkness and a scattering of lights. Running with Andrew. No room to manoeuvre. He was the first. She was the second. Siblings first and last. He is coming through the window and she is gasping for air. No words for this. No words.

****

Whilst Meg was gasping for air, Andrew's epilepsy worsened and his delusions grew. He kept walking away in search of a place where people would appreciate he was a martyr. Each morning over breakfast he addressed his parents. 'Mother and Father, I am the son of God, I am the Way, the Truth and the Life. When are you coming to church, you sinners? Follow me. I will lead the way!'

Vasili and Jane despaired. They had no more ideas. Andrew was beyond them and they were losing Meg. There was nowhere that could accommodate Andrew. He visited an 'epileptic colony' to bring the Word to the residents. He stayed there for several months before a girl fell pregnant by him. He was disturbing their peace and they threw him out. A sexual life was out of the question. Surely his parents knew that. They knew no such thing. Where could Andrew find a place to lay his head?

Their ill child was fiercely independent. He rented bed sitting-rooms, got casual work on building sites, which lasted until the next *grand mal* led to dismissal. He was strong as an ox and not afraid of hard work. He stayed in monasteries. In a Dorchester friary he was welcomed by the monks and worked in their garden. Andrew wrote to his parents that he was trying to persuade them to let him 'bring a dog inside' but that they had refused his request. He'd made a wooden cross and wanted to live there for ever. He realised the error of his ways. He was not the son of God after all, he was not Rasputin. He wished to become a monk and he would have to give up all his possessions. Please could Vasili and Jane sell the drum kit and the big amp. 'Rest assured, all. I am at last perfectly sane and would like you to visit soon. God bless you.' The grand mals, though, became too much even for the gentle monks of Dorchester. They could not take the responsibility and yet again Andrew was without a roof over his head.

He roamed the country far and wide, paying his way from a trust fund established by his maternal grandmother, Ruth, which became his at the age of twenty-one. Andrew's letters home combined loftiness and good humour. He sounded like Vasili, writing that he had 'business to attend to' or of his latest girlfriend's behavior being 'irresponsible and irra-tional'. He used the psychiatric terminology he and Meg had learned from their father without understanding the words. In one letter he wrote that he was in the middle of a 'nervous breakdown' and would soon be having another, so everyone 'should watch out!' He was engaged in the academic study of Christianity, psychology, astrology, Russian mysticism and science and was beginning 'to look into empiricism and rationality'. His meter had been broken into.

In the summer of 1975, when Andrew was twenty-five years old, he wrote to Vasili and Jane from a home in Plymouth for adults with difficulties:

Dear Mum and Dad,

How are you? I just can't think what to put down. Today one of the members left. He was a friend of mine which was a pitty. Today I've been getting weeds out of the mangle field with a mattock. Then had our siesta.

On Saturday the village had a carnival. I went as John the Baptist. Dermot, the friend who left, went as Goliath with JonJon, the little boy went as David, and Shealla went as a nurse. I got first prize, as I was one alone and not a couple.

We paraded around the town and came back. I went bare footed which made it a bit of a bind in the field with thistles. Jeff the Harp our vicar was there and I asked him to repent and blessed him. I was at one of the sideshows. I had to stick my head through a board and have eggs thrown at me.

It was quite good. It was great when we marched through the village. We played the drums, trumpets, etc. I really felt grand.

Have you sold my amp?

So Long. Bye.

Andrew

Vasili and Jane were reassured. Jane typed out Andrew's letter and sent it to Meg's latest address, hoping that the news of Andrew settled might persuade her to return home. Jane had lost count of the bedsits Meg had lived in over the past five years. When Meg received the copy of the letter from her mother, she was in North London. She had grown thin and looked much older than her twenty-three years.

Meg cried over the letter. She was struck by Andrew's

wisdom and the humour she had forgotten. 'I was one alone and not a couple.' 'I was at one of the sideshows.' Egg in his face. Egos and superegos. Shouting beneath the table at their parents' parties. Such exuberance they had shared.

Andrew knew that he would never be accepted. He was a sideshow for the amusement of others, so he blessed people, even when they were cruel and despicable. Andrew was an infinitely better person than the boys who had kicked and punched and jeered at him. There he was, larger than life and over six feet tall, head and shoulders above the rest of the carnival. He played comedy's clown for all he was worth. There was her brother, with his best foot forward, stepping out in life's parade while she was sitting silent in the shadows. Come, play your fife and drum! The big man feels grand, really grand. And there was Alexis, the little man, also a fairground figure. He is tumbling and juggling and playing the strongman. He laughs and cries and throws his hands in the air in mock defeat. Andrew and Alexis.

Meg was in a spiral spinning round and around. She had no strength. So long, Andrew. Bye for now. Be well, Meg whispered from the lower depths. She was a nondescript.

February, 1977

Huge, gut-wrenching shouts were coming from the break-fast room, which stank of sweat and drugs. Vasili and Jane were in and out of Andrew's room, day and night. They were sombre, appalled, ashamed they could not help their son in his agony. The doctor assured them everything was being done. The young man would rally, but Jane was not convinced. Would the end be as it was in the beginning?

In the middle of the third night Andrew was rushed to hospital in an ambulance. Meg had returned from one of her bed sitting-rooms to be at her brother's side, but Andrew had lost consciousness by the time she arrived. A massive brain haemorrhage had been set in train by a lifetime of falling over. Meg stayed at her brother's side.

In the evening Vasili returned home to get some sleep and make arrangements at work, while Jane and Meg waited in the relatives' room. Andrew would be in surgery for several hours. A woman of about her own age asked Meg, 'So what are you in for?' as if she were in prison. 'It's horrible here, isn't it?' she said. She kept asking Meg, 'What are you in for?' Was there something wrong with the woman? 'My brother is dying. He is dying. That is what I am in for.' She looked with contempt at the woman and hated herself for not being kinder.

Andrew was on life support and for several days his family gathered and re-gathered at his bedside. Jane sat on one side, Vasili and Meg on the other. Meg believed she belonged at her father's side. He needed her. Jane and Vasili had grown apart over the years. Maybe Alexis was sitting beside her mother. Yes, there he was. He had gone out of his way to be here for his daughter-in-law, Jane, who had the look of open fields. He was chanting, his hand touching Andrew's forehead, tracing the sign of the cross in his final hours. Meg was glad her mother was comforted.

Jane was with her first child, on her own, when he died. Vasili and Meg had returned home for something to eat and her mother phoned while Vasili was preparing dinner, which he carried on cooking after the news of Andrew's death. Meg could not understand how her father could behave as if nothing had happened. Much later she understood it was his way of coping.

The next day they went to see Andrew's body, which was laid out in the hospital mortuary. Nobody had prepared them and Meg stopped in horror at the sight. Andrew's mouth was wide open and rigid. The ventilator had filled his whole mouth and the nurses had not had time to close it before rigor mortis set in. Was that true? Meg wondered. Surely they could have tried harder. Draped over her brother's body and touching the floor on each side of the slab, there was a purple velvet pall with a gigantic golden cross down the middle. Why on earth had they laid her brother out in this way? The fire of grievance threatened to break out.

The chapel attached to the Surrey crematorium was half full at Andrew's funeral. There were relatives and family friends, neighbours from the village and some of Vasili's colleagues. After the coffin and the mourners had moved slowly down the aisle and everyone had taken their seats, the vicar spoke of Andrew:

I think we must all be feeling an emotional conflict. We have come with thankfulness, for Andrew and for the pain of his injuries, his physical and mental frustrations, the extreme limitations and his vulnerability. They have come to an end and he has been released into God's peace.

He talked of Andrew's intelligence that shone through the damage to his brain. He paid tribute to his spirit and immense courage, of the character so 'tragically imprisoned in a damaged body.' Everyone who knew Andrew developed a warm and lasting affection for him, he said. He finished his address with these words:

I wonder in all this whether Andrew was not nearer to the heart of Christ's wisdom and love than some of us with our worldly standards. 'The foxes have holes and the birds have their nests but the Son of Man has not where to lay his head.'

Our Lord said to the young man asking what he must do to have eternal life: 'Go and sell all that thou hast and give to the poor and come and follow me.'

The whole world was sobbing for Meg's brother. After the funeral, not for the last time, she gave away all her clothes, apart from the black ones she wore that day. There was no God, but there were foxes which ran in and out of cover. She left home shortly after the funeral to resume her bed sitting-room existence, blowing hither and thither but with freshly forged iron in her soul. Meg continued to lose her way badly.

Her memory played tricks. The little she could see of the past was tiny bits and pieces. She could barely make them out. They were like dust motes lit up in a sunbeam's path but in the absence of the sun. She returned to the darkness inside solitary rooms. She could not think straight. Sentences came out all wrong on the page. When Andrew died, Meg's heart and soul stopped dead in their dual sibling tracks.

****

1992

Meg lifted her head. She realised she had not been able to capture that girl in the darkness. She gazed at the letters, the grades that haunted her, and then tore them into pieces and threw them into the wastepaper basket. All that time she had spent running away from the boy she had loved so much, but whose attention was forever elsewhere. Her neck was hurting. Meg stretched. She still ached for Andrew's presence. To imagine what it might have felt like to be inside Andrew's head was an idea Meg had only ever fleetingly entertained, before putting it out of her mind. She had been so caught up in her brother's very being, to have put herself in his place would surely have been one step too far. But she had not done him justice and probably never would. Was this the time when she might draw a line and call it a day?

No, not quite yet.

11

A sailor dress

In Vasili's final years at the nursing home Meg and her father had drunk champagne when she visited. His room was on the ground floor of a pleasant red-brick house, his window overlooking a lawn and a cherry tree. The room was L-shaped and gave you the sense that there were still some corners to be turned, even after two major strokes.

When Meg visited her father, travelling some distance from a bed sitting-room in East London, she talked with him about her life. 'I've begun seeing a therapist, Dad. She is kind and stern.' This pleased her father. 'By your voice she sounds gentle,' he said, 'and that is good.'

'My own analyst was rather fearsome,' he added with a twinkle in his eye. Vasili did not know the time of day and could not feed himself, but he could still talk lucidly about psychoanalysis. 'I felt like a small boy in the presence of a very formidable mother. She used to scold me for being too tentative. I wondered if she was going to give me a hundred lines or stand me in the corner!' They had laughed together. Vasili was glad Meg had found a therapist who was less fierce.

Meg brought smoked salmon and brie, small bottles of liqueurs and a half bottle of champagne at weekends. Vasili was a little old man with a tender, bewildered expression on his face. He stroked Meg's hands like they were new to him. He boasted to the nurses. 'My daughter has a BA in

English and she writes poetry!', even though Meg was still working as a temp in offices all over London.

Vasili had decided to die early one autumn two years ago. He stopped taking food and faded away without pain or rage. Meg was not with him when he died, but the next morning she said her quiet goodbyes. Her father looked like a child, fast asleep and at peace in a comfortable bed, tucked in by his mother. The funeral was a small gathering at the crematorium where Andrew came to rest but, as Vasili was an atheist, there was no religious ceremony. Outside there were flowers, including a small spray from Jane, who did not attend the funeral. She and Vasili broke up shortly after Andrew died and they kept the details of that story to themselves.

Meg missed her father too much to begin writing about him. Maybe one day she would tell his story, but not yet. Since Vasili died Meg had begun to know her mother better. Andrew, Alexis and her father had filled her imagination and there had been little space left for her mother. She had blamed her parents for what went wrong in her childhood and yet she wondered if they could have done anything more. Another child might not have become so identified with her ill sibling, might have been more robust and reacted differently. Her self-obliteration in the face of the epilepsy could not have been anticipated.

The unfinished story of Alexis was on her desk and a story about Andrew and herself was beginning to emerge. The disappointment at never having been able to find characters in books who remotely resembled Andrew and herself did not have to matter so much any more. She might find comfort now in Wordsworth's inoffensive child, his 'idiot boy', or Dostoevsky's gentle Prince Myshkin.

Meg went to bed feeling reasonably secure of her recollections.

****

Saturday was mild. The June sun was breaking gently through the clouds in the early afternoon, as Meg was setting up a stall of breads and cheeses and several large plastic bowls, full to the brim with salads. She was also serving some Pimms she had made herself, after a recipe her mother had used for parties. Thin slices of apple and orange and sprigs of mint floated on the surface of the bowls. The organisers had bought the ingredients, so all Meg had to do was mix them in roughly the right quantities. The Pimms tasted good, a little strong perhaps, but full of fruit and sun.

The concert would begin at three. There was to be a calypso band, a string quartet and a solo jazz singer, all of whom had offered their services gratis. People living round the common had been glad, on the whole, to hear of the coming restoration of the bandstand, where music had not been heard for years. Some residents were worried there might be too much noise, but they were assured it was only licensed for music at the weekends between midday and seven in the evening.

The domed bandstand was a listed building and over a hundred years old. Neglect had weakened the structure and led to its being in danger of imminent collapse. Meg admired the resilience of a structure which had withstood adverse weather and general wear and tear for so many years. For the concert the bandstand had been shored up with scaffolding, but you could see its outline, the eight pairs of struts, once painted dusky pink, but now faded and peeling.

The players in the calypso band were setting up their instruments on stage and people were already gathering round. There was a large tent to the side of the bandstand, where the musicians were assembling. Around the whole area a temporary fence had been erected and there was a small entrance, where two people were selling tickets. On stage the all-male band gathered, four musicians playing trumpet, acoustic guitars, steel-pan and bongos, and a singer. The tall singer introduced the band, who hailed from Antigua, but had lived in London for decades. Everyone clapped as he began to sing of islands and sunlight, emigrants and drifters, and a few people, soon joined by others, began to dance in the sandy space in front of the bandstand. Elderly people sat on the benches in the shade of the large trees.

Meg spotted her friends, Robert and Elaine, and their child Dom moving over the common towards the party. They were a hundred yards away and were waving as Meg raised her glass and smiled in their direction. Dom began to run on ahead of his parents towards her stall and Meg caught him in her arms, holding the small boy aloft and twirling him around. Robert walked over and took hold of Dom, cautioning him 'Mind Meg's neck, Dom – you know it's a bit poorly.' Dom looked a little worried, but Meg assured him her neck was fine. One of the organisers came over to take Meg's place, as she had been on the stall for a couple of hours now and it was time for her to enjoy the party.

They ate and drank and danced, Dom weaving in and out of their legs or being whirled around by Robert and Elaine. After about half an hour Elaine asked Meg if she minded being left for a while, as she and Robert had promised Dom they'd buy him a toy in one of the gift shops on the other side of the common.

There was a break between bands and you could hear the string quartet tuning up in the tent. Meg walked out of the enclosed area and sat down beneath a tree, where she still had a good view of the bandstand. Gazing around at the huge expanse of common, with so many roads criss-crossing it in every direction, Meg had a sense that she might be finding herself somewhere at this hub of connections. The clock tower on the other side of the common was also a hub where many roads met and diverged every which way. The Junction station was another, where many lines and trains converged.

Meg often talked with friends about the common and its environs. It was, she said, a very 'frenetic, chaotic' place, and yet that never sounded quite right, as if she were only critical of where she had chosen to live. You might look at it another way. For much of her life she had been directionless, so maybe it was apt that she found herself in a place of many, if confusing, possibilities.

Her grandfather had, after all, lived near the crossroads of Central Asia, with the Silk Road at its heart. The world was a caravanserai with many openings, a plethora of exits and entrances. You arrived and you left. You left and arrived. You might glimpse the Silk Road or join it from a byroad, your head held high, or choose to stray off the highway, seeking somewhere less exposed. To settle might be a good idea but this did not have to mean settling down. Like Alexis, she had read and enjoyed Robert Louis Stevenson's *Treasure Island*, and later the story of his travels on a donkey in France. With a small pack on his back he had journeyed and meandered along. He had slept on summer nights beneath the stars.

She did not have to leave Andrew behind. She was much too close to his memory for that and there was still work to do, in terms of seeing him with more clarity, recognising him as the small boy and vulnerable man that he was. She would bear him in mind forever, but that was all she could do. She had embodied his illness for far too long. When she studied Eliot's *Middlemarch*, she had taken these words to heart:

If we had a keen vision and feeling of all ordinary human life, it would be like hearing the grass grow and the squirrel's heart beat, and we should die of that roar which lies on the other side of silence.

Meg had cried for the existence of such a tender thought in the world, and yet she had never been sure what 'ordinary human life' might be. The roar of the traffic crossing the common and skirting the edges was muted, but never far away. She had located herself at the heart of Andrew's illness, which had terrified and arrested her, and she must get some distance now, so that simple compassion might take the place of conflicted emotions. The memory of Andrew might then become more real, more measured, more ordinary. A small boy might begin to emerge.

Earlier in the day Meg had discovered a menu card in one of Vasili's boxes, recording her birthday dinner on Friday, 21 June 1963. That was her eleventh birthday, when Vasili and Jane took her for a celebration at The Bridge House, a restaurant in the Surrey hills. Andrew had not been well and they had left him with a nurse for the evening. She recalled the happiness of sitting on her own with her parents. The menu card was signed on either side of the dishes, 'With love from Mummy' and 'With love from Daddy' and there were crosses beside the food she chose. Chilled pineapple juice, followed by Chicken and fresh vegetables and for the third course, Fresh Strawberries and Cream at three shillings and sixpence extra. Forty years on, Meg realised her tastes had not changed that much.

In the early seventies, eight years after Meg's eleventh birthday, another party had gathered at The Bridge House, to celebrate Andrew's twenty-first birthday. The guests sitting round a circular table were Andrew, Meg, Vasili, Jane, Laurie and Betty (the last being close friends of the family).

Andrew's party was a small gathering but there were, in addition, two invisible presences at the table, who floated around. These were the spirits of the past, and if you studied the scene carefully, you could make out Alexis (who could pass for any age) and beside him the tall form of Hazel, a presiding spirit who gazed affectionately at this family gathering.

Between Vasili and Jane sat Andrew, who was flourishing a large silver key made of silver foil, presented to him by his father. He waved the key like a magician, grinning from ear to ear. He behaved like the host, beaming at his guests and nodding his head sagely. He was not Rasputin

or Jesus or even a monk. He was simply Andrew and everyone was thankful. He kept standing up to make little
speeches, asking everyone if they were having a good time,
and if they weren't, he'd send for the Manager pronto, he'd
see about things.

The table was littered with crackers and little plastic gifts,
and everyone was wearing a paper hat. Meg was nineteen
and she was wearing a white and gold sari to cover herself
up, conceal the extra weight she was carrying. The sari she
had bought in the Kings Road and this was the first time
she had worn it. Meg was sitting between Laurie and Betty,
who had both turned to Meg. They were asking her about
the latest music and fashion and her 'lovely sari'. The Kings
Road? Meg felt lumpish in their presence. They were so
trim. She bitterly regretted that she was no longer elfin and
slight, that she had grown so heavy. Laurie asked her about
Alexis's art collection, all those Constables, he smiled. What
a collection it was! 'But, you know, Meg, maybe it was a
good thing that your grandfather had to sell them, especially the great *Chain Pier*. Now everyone can go and see it
at the Tate!' Yes, that was a good thing, Meg agreed.

Andrew's twenty-first had ended with everyone, even her
father who hated to dance, joining Andrew on the floor.
There had been no live music but records were playing –
The Beatles, The Four Tops, The Supremes, The Rolling
Stones. She was the last to stand up. Andrew danced with
Betty, Vasili with Jane and Laurie with Meg. *Here, There and
Everywhere* began to play. The dancers glided or stumbled,
graceful or out of step. Alexis and Hazel were in among the
dancers, invisible mythic presences woven into the pattern
and fabric of the dancers' lives. No-one fell down. Later on
Andrew would have a heart-stopping *grand mal* in the
middle of the dance floor and the party would jolt to a halt,
the delicate weave of family life broken up yet again, but for
the moment the dance and the pattern held good.

****

Meg sighed. She was getting stiff sitting against the tree. There was a slight chill in the air as the day moved towards dusk.

She saw her friends returning from the shops. Dom was flourishing an ice-cream. Lucky boy! Elaine had coffee for Meg and some almond macaroons which they shared. The string quartet had finished and a small girl stood on the stage. She was to sing some folk songs from her country. The girl was about eight years old and wore a sailor dress. She seemed very nervous and her mother jumped up onto the stage to hold her hand and whisper some encouraging words.

Meg recalled dancing in *Sea Piece* when she was nine and meeting Alexis later that afternoon. She remembered the girl with the misshapen head and the Sart doctor who had chanted over her at the beginning of the century, whilst Alexis looked on. Here was a child of roughly the same age as those girls from the past, those earlier selves. And now the girl was beginning to sing. Meg did not understand the words, but the child's voice was beautiful and the tune lilting and sad and hopeful by turn.

Standing between Robert and Elaine, with Dom on his father's shoulders, Meg sensed that in this girl's presence something in herself was beginning to change.

About the Author

Gill Gregory taught in adult education before being awarded a PhD in English at Birkbeck College, University of London. For the past ten years she has worked as a lecturer at The University of Notre Dame. She has reviewed for the *Times Literary Supplement* and other publications include a monograph on Adelaide Procter, *Poetry, Feminism & Fathers* (Ashgate Publishing). Her first collection of poetry, *In Slow Woods*, is published by Rufus Books.

'Gill Gregory's poems have the economy of proverb combined with an emotional and intellectual force that resonates far beyond their spare lines.' *Andrew Teverson*

'Subtle, intelligent, luminous writing that registers histories owned and imagined.' *Deryn Rees-Jones*

About this book

The Sound of Turquoise is about the child I once was who lives on in my memory. She is the girl I have found in my imagination. In this third person narrative Meg, the central figure, is in many ways blessed with a warm and cultured family. She is, though, preoccupied to the point of obsession with her elder brother, Andrew's epilepsy and the intense fear generated by his seizures. She is bound up with his very being to the extent that her more ordinary life becomes unreal to her.

In writing this book I have summoned the figure of my Russian grandfather, Alexis – a boy who escaped death in Tashkent in 1904 and went on to forge an adventurous career in England as a doctor, farmer, art collector and bon viveur. Even though I only met Alexis once he became my talisman and leitmotif, functioning as a counterbalance to the disturbance of my brother's epilepsy. The child, Meg, imagines the resilient, healthy boy for whom nothing and no-one stood in his way.

My book is an experiment in life writing. As a third person narrative it is not memoir or autobiography. The story is based in real histories but it also maps the invisible pathways, the haunted terrains that this child, who is myself, keeps on bearing in mind.

Gill Gregory, 2009

Award Winning Life Writing, Memoir and Biography
from Kingston University Press Ltd

Gill Gregory's book *The Sound of Turquoise* won first place in the prestigious Life Writing, Memoir and Biography competition held by Kingston University Press and judged by Rachel Cusk, Kathryn Hughes and Hanif Kureishi.

More praise for *The Sound of Turquoise*:

'A gripping and very moving book, a family story chronicling the effects upon a sensitive young woman of two family tragedies, one close at hand, the other in pre-revolutionary Russia. I found it hard to put down and am sure that other readers will feel the same.' *Leonee Ormond*

Other competition winners include:

Being Caribbean in Carmarthenshire Maggie Harris, *Petrol* Martina Evans and *Caribbean Chemistry* Christopher Vanier

200 urf
150 milk
200 mrsca (oils)

Also published by KUP Ltd:

Caribbean Chemistry Tales from St Kitts
Christopher Vanier

Ah, to be an embryo again.

Vanier's story begins where we all begin: conception. Funny and engaging, this story of self-discovery recalls the mischief of Vanier's childhood: sneaking out to the cinema after school hours, disastrous experiments involving various acids and a rocket. Is this boy lost in the plain sailing of childhood or can he turn his curiosity into Caribbean Chemistry?

A rare view of the emigrants tale, of breaking the barriers of identity and finding them again, told candidly in language rich enough to eat: "Breadfruit, breadnut, bamboo, lignum vitae, marouba, weedee, and calabash."

ISBN: 978-1-899999-45-3   416pp